Date Due

~~SPK~~			
SV 000 585	Due 6-12-92		

LIP-READING

TEACH YOURSELF
LIP-READING

Second Printing

By

OLIVE M. WYATT

CHARLES C THOMAS · PUBLISHER
Springfield · Illinois · U.S.A.

Published and Distributed by
CHARLES C THOMAS • PUBLISHER
BANNERSTONE HOUSE
301-327 East Lawrence Avenue, Springfield, Illinois, U.S.A.
NATCHEZ PLANTATION HOUSE
735 North Atlantic Boulevard, Fort Lauderdale, Florida, U.S.A.

First Printing, 1961
© 1960, by The English Universities Press Ltd.

Second Printing, 1969
© *1969, by* CHARLES C THOMAS • PUBLISHER
Library of Congress Catalog Card Number: 61-4731

Printed in the United States of America
N-1

CONTENTS

PART I: PUTTING LIFE INTO LIP-READING

LESSON

INTRODUCTION

DOROTHY H. KUTNER
President of the London League of the Hard of
Hearing

To be asked to write an introduction to Miss Wyatt's book "Teach Yourself Lip-Reading" is indeed a compliment which I very much appreciate.

As a teacher of lip-reading of many years' standing, I have naturally read many text books on this subject, analysed them and adapted them for my own use and that of my students. There are many aspects of the subject, and each plays a vital part in the final adjustment of the student to life, where "eyes must take the place of ears".

Miss Wyatt is indeed a brave and very generous woman to share with the world of deafness her secret of success. This generosity is what makes her book such a very valuable addition to the existing small selection of books dealing with this subject.

Happiness and geniality just shine out on each page, as her well tried plans are laid out for all to see and use. She starts as one might with a child, but her simple methods are expressed in such a way that she encourages the most intelligent to get down to an arduous but very much worthwhile job. She does not hide the fact that the acquisition of lip-reading is by no means easy or rapid, but she certainly makes it an interesting goal to aim at, with very satisfying and useful results. Unlike so many teachers, she treats her subject and her students in an adult way, and above all with a delightful humour. This is no dry-as-dust subject, it is a living thing for people who are very much alive.

The personal interests of her students are studied and admirably catered for, in an interesting manner.

Miss Wyatt certainly does not allow the grass to grow under her feet, nor under the feet of her students. She herself is an example of what can be and has been done, by the hard of hearing themselves, if they will avail themselves of the help and advice in the pages of this book.

FOREWORD

THIS book just happened.

I feel I must speak of this quite personally, even intimately, to my readers, for as I have written the book many thousands—nay, millions—of the deaf have entered my heart through the door that opened with my own need as a deaf woman, on the needs and wants of those others who seemed to think I had something to give.

How long this book has been working in my subconscious mind, as I became increasingly deaf over a long period, I do not know. Even as a child with my sister, I pretended being blind, then deaf-and-dumb, and we gave ourselves some practical idea of what such afflictions could be like. And I have been teaching in one way and another since I was very young.

As the Head of a large Preparatory Department feeding the local boys' and girls' Grammar Schools, I spent a fighting and winning life to the end that little children might learn to live abundantly through the adventure of education, by a drawing out of the possibilities within them rather than by a ramming in from outside of something that somebody thought they ought to have. My experience proved this to be the most effective and worth-while method of teaching.

When I began to find, before the days of such

efficient hearing aids as we have now, that my hearing was so quickly deteriorating as to be hampering my work, I found my experimental mind and methods automatically seeking to compensate. Walking into my reading lesson with ten-year-olds one morning, I made an unusual introduction to the lesson.

"You're not going to read to me today," I said. "You're going to read to a class of blind children" (soliciting their initial interest in the 'pretence' through the blind as better known and commanding greater interest than the deaf). "Remember, no dull voices, lazy tongues, even dull faces, when you read to the blind. A dull face means a dull voice, even if you can't see the face. Be natural, of course, but choose something that makes you feel enthusiastic."

Off we went—and was I pleased with the result!

At our next reading lesson: "Today we shall read to deaf children. No lazy lips, no lazy tongues; mouths wide enough and long enough to be seen into for what is going on there; and enjoy what you read to them, and let them see that you are doing so."

Another day: "That old man at the back of the hall, in the corner. He's almost asleep already. Say something specially that you think will interest the tired old man as much as you see you are interesting those in front of you. He might perhaps like to think about a question that refers to what you were saying when you discovered he was 'dropping off'." And so on.

Then, when I was becoming increasingly deaf, I

found myself saying, as in a dream, "I have decided to retire"—nine years prematurely. I became involved in work for the blind, but this was to be only temporary. Thus, for the first time since I set out for my first post, I was to live alone—exhausted from the years of fighting, deaf and with a hearing aid that was no longer serviceable. A friend made me one of the best aids I have ever had for tête-à-têtes, out of rubber tubing, a funnel costing sixpence in a chain store, and the rounded end of an old fountain pen with a hole bored in it. Total cost, 1/6!

Thus equipped I attended the inaugural meeting of a club for hard-of-hearing persons, where I hoped I would be able to get practice in lip-reading. Being known as a retired teacher who was learning lip-reading privately, I was asked to fill a gap in the programme. We had an impromptu lip-reading game. There was a collection of objects, whose shapes were easily recognisable, on the table, and round this and a little distance away was seated a 'horseshoe' of members. The objects were clearly named on the speaking lips from which the sound-movements could be read; the objects themselves providing the clues to what was being spoken about. So the 'spotting clue words' method was born—and the idea that the deaf have something to give to the deaf.

In helping others to practise I became at once a teacher and a learner. Another teacher joined me in studying and working out the now obvious possibilities of our method. Lesson by lesson it got worked out. written as lesson notes for home use, developed into class work as requested, and now it has been further amplified into a comprehensive book.

I hope that, in writing out of my own experience and that of others with whom I have been working on experimental methods of turning our necessary study into a hobby, I shall have stimulated interest in others who are afflicted in the same way. Maybe this interest will be shown in self-expression through articles in *The Silent World* (the official organ for the deaf) or through the correspondence columns of the Press, so that we may all try to find different angles of approach to our subject and hope to give hearing people a better understanding of our problems, which are not yet really appreciated.

For those who enjoy social groupings, 'The Little Fellowships of Common Interests' will prove a great help and addition to life as well as to lessons. They create a togetherness which can greatly enhance the lives of the lonely and add abundance of interest to those who look for it, especially to those who have the conscious will to conquer, in some special direction or other, the handicap they suffer. And interest is the key to progress.

From my own experience I commend such experimentings to any to whom they may appeal; and, as an old man recently said to me: "May the Blessing of the One Who Knows" go with them.

THANKS

I WOULD especially thank those who have been working out these ideas with me for frankly expressing their difficulties, and for offering, frankly, their criticisms—the critical student who first inspired this work; the frustrated student who first encouraged the development of it; and the complete stranger who, on nothing more than an introductory article, came many miles to study the development of it, and has introduced it to others. I would also thank the reader of my manuscript and those who typed the whole. So much have they helped me to enjoy experimenting that I hope others may enjoy the results, and perhaps be encouraged by them to make experiments of their own, for it is this delight in the experimental that takes the drudgery from lip-reading when we have to learn it in middle and later years. If we never become perfect lip-readers (who does?) we can at least get enough to keep us interested in other people, and other people interested in us, and ourselves relevant in conversation with those who are so. That, generally speaking, is enough to start with, but if we like really to work at our lip-reading, practising daily, as children do at school and at home, why shouldn't "Practice make perfect"?

Special thanks are due to the Publishers who have allowed me to use the passages that I have selected for our use. These selections, too, "just came" to be recognised as giving point to our studies and enabling the charted forms to be prepared with each selection for use as mirror or partner practice by the "Teach Yourself" student.

ACKNOWLEDGEMENTS

To Messrs. Rankin Bros. Ltd., and Donald Hughes for permission to reproduce extracts from *The Chippendale Chairs* and *A Song of Love*. Michael Joseph Ltd., for permission to reproduce extracts from *The Snow Goose* by Paul Gallico. William Heinemann Ltd., for permission to reproduce an extract from *Wind, Sand and Stars* by Antoine de Saint-Exupéry. W. Somerset Maugham and Messrs. W. Heinemann Ltd., for permission to reproduce an extract from *Sanatorium*. Jonathan Cape Ltd., for permission to reproduce an extract from *The Spring of Joy* by Mary Webb. Jarrolds Ltd., for permission to reproduce an extract from *The Day is Ours* by Hilda Lewis. J. M. Watkins for permission to reproduce *A Mystic's Story* from Meister Eckhart.

The copyright holders of *An Old World Creed* by M. Aumonier and *Bees in November* by Edith Allen are unknown and these verses are reproduced with apologies.

HOW TO USE THE BOOK

THE study of lip-reading, or, as it is better called, speech-reading, is often found in the early stages to bring nothing but a sense of fatigue. Thus many people who have started it hopefully have soon given it up. That is why I suggest that you treat it as a hobby rather than as a task that you must grind away at.

Those who study lip-reading seem to me to divide themselves into two groups: the deafened and totally deaf who live alone, and those of them who live with others. To whichever group you belong, I would suggest that most of the work must be done by yourself in practice, anywhere and everywhere. While I would in no way decry formal study under a trained teacher, I must emphasise that it is this constant practice that does most of the teaching; it encourages learners to be their own teachers in always trying to find out the how, why and wherefore of the thing. All that we need for teaching ourselves lip-reading is a little courage and common sense and a good deal of spirit and perseverance, and the facility will 'come'.

Do not attempt detailed study of this book to begin with. First read it through and get the gist of it, then settle down to lessons and practice.

To hard-of-hearing folk, especially the older ones, words have hitherto been a matter of spelling. You must now re-orient yourself on the basis of PHONETICS; that is, you have to become conscious of the SHAPE and MOVEMENT seen on the mouth, in relation to their SOUND. You must always remember that what letters SAY is all-important—what they are called doesn't much matter.

To start with, you must form the habit of concentrating on the speaker's lips ('the speaker' may be someone else, or yourself as you practise with a mirror). Later you will take in the general facial expression as a guide to the type of conversation—whether it is sad or humorous, serious or frivolous.

But concentration does not necessarily mean tension. Work always in a *relaxed* state of mind. It doesn't matter if you 'don't get it' at first. Everything will be registering itself in your mind, whether consciously or subconsciously, and it will all be used by the conscious mind in time, as the educational principles behind the lessons work out in practice.

You should not consider each lesson finished when you have come to the end of your 'study period' on it. If you have someone to help you, either hearing or hard-of-hearing, you should rebuild some part of the lesson, without using aids, in the form of DICTATION. If you are working alone, then speak your selected passage into a mirror, checking up 'shape and movement in relation to sound' as you do so—in the classroom we should call this TRANSCRIPTION. Words or phrases of which you are not sure should be respoken into the mirror, and the shapes should be carefully and accurately pronounced.

The hard-of-hearing generally *know*, in the back of their minds, how to lip-read, and often do it without realising. The purpose of these lessons is to bring this knowledge to the threshold of your consciousness, and to make you use it consciously until 'practice makes perfect' and your use of it becomes really unconscious.

This book is meant for those who have had hearing once; for those who still have some that may decrease, or who can still be helped by a hearing-aid; for those who because of advancing years would prefer to learn informally rather than in a class; for those who, living alone, still refuse to be defeated; for those who, joining a club, wish to enter with others into the practice of this their hobby; for those who want to make a first line of defence against possible or oncoming isolation, 'the desolation of being shut out'. For all these the writer has worked at these experimental pages, and to all these she dedicates her book with her love.

PART I

INTRODUCTION TO PART I

THE most practical approach to lip-reading, especially for those who live alone, is by what is called the SYNTHETIC method. The aim of this is that the 'reader' should be able to get the gist of each phrase or sentence, rather than have to interpret each sound-shape as it comes along and then build all the shapes into words and all the words into a sentence. In this book, I use the ANALYTICAL method, the sound-by-sound one, which is much more exhausting to use for long, only as a means by which you can check up what you are learning by the easier method: you learn to get a grasp of the whole and to break it down into units only occasionally, when you feel you must.

We come as adults to learn lip-reading as if we were children learning to read the printed page. How do children learn to read nowadays? These hierogly-phics called letters do not live *as* letters. Children come to their reading with interest and freshness because their letters live in words, in chatter and story, in poetry and song. Children's interest in letters as such then develops through words—the picture-words representing things, the words they have used in sentences of their own speech-making—and through more and more words, their scope expanded by an increasing knowledge of what the sounds mean, they go on into more and more adventurous thinking and talking, reading and writing.

So I begin at the finished article, and dissect it, so to speak, only in order to find out how we have arrived. To us, as to children, letters and words prove uninteresting (to start with, at least) apart from the sentences and paragraphs which make up the subject of our study. It is only after we have read a book that we can enjoy studying and dissecting a chosen part in relation to the whole.

Then begin on the lessons of Part I, and 'he who hath ears to hear, let him hear'—let him hear (or rather read) how as well as what to learn. Learn how to turn your silence to good purpose and to find a positive side to your handicap.

LESSON 1

A Simple Approach to Shape and Movement

BEFORE you start studying each time, get out the one simple tool that you will need to learn and practise with—a hand-mirror in which you will observe and watch the shapes made by the various sounds.

Your aim in this first lesson is to become conscious of SHAPE and MOVEMENT as you watch your lips in the mirror. Remember that letters say something in relation to their sound.

We begin with a simple, factual lay-out of the fundamentals that you must learn to recognise (and you *will* learn, with practice!).

1. (*a*) Form the shape of the short vowels in relation to their sound, i.e.: Say 'apple'. Take a breath; hold it; form the shape for 'a' as in 'apple'. Let out the breath with the sound of 'a'.

(*b*) Then treat similarly:

> 'e' as in 'egg' or 'elephant'
> 'i' as in 'ink'
> 'o' as in 'orange'
> 'u' as in '*u*p with the *u*mbrella'

(You are sounding them, aren't you? Not naming them.)

(*c*) Now make these vowel-sounds again, watching the movement on your lips in the same way, in your hand-mirror.

2. (*a*) Take a breath; say 'pot'. Form your mouth for another breath, held ready gently to explode 'p' as in 'pot'. (Mandy, in the film of that name* in which a born-deaf child learned speech, puffed a candle-flame to get the sound of 'p'). Be very careful not to sound it 'per'—just enough to flicker the flame is as much as you want.

(*b*) Now discover the make-up of: pat, pet, pit, pot, putt.

The word	the sound	movement and shape in the sound	movement and shape in the word
pat	a	pa	pat
pet	e	pe	pet
pit	i	pi	pit
pot	o	po	pot
putt	u	pu	putt

(*c*) Practise short sounds like this into your mirror as you might see them on a film's screen at slow speed, e.g.:

$$bat = ba/t$$
$$fat = fa/t$$

---

* "Mandy" is the film of the book *The Day is Ours*, by H. Lewis, published by Jarrolds.

$$mat = ma/t$$
$$bed = be/d$$
$$fed = fe/d$$
$$led = le/d$$

and so on. You will come to realise for yourself that this is how all speech is built up; as you speak shape and movement with breath behind them so you make the sound of words in sentences.

You will find the little books I recommend in Lesson 3 very useful for keeping you conscious of this principle until it becomes automatic. One of my pupils keeps them handy and uses them at odd moments, such as when she is waiting for the kettle to boil!

*　　　　*　　　　*

This first lesson is rather like a map. It needn't bother you much, but may be useful for reference from time to time. The idea now is to get on.

There are full charts of sounds and movements for your reference in Appendix 1. They were especially invited by a determined student.

Practice Work on Lesson 1

You can carry on with this practice work as part of the lesson, or treat it as "homework", or both.

Aim

To relieve the strain of concentration, at this

stage, by going a bit informal, and burlesquing the matter with tongue-twisters and absurdities.

1. Concentrate only on the shape of 'a' in the following tongue-twister.

(a) If a plaid-clad caddy-laddie's daddy/had a fad for adding/ Would the plaid-clad caddy laddie's daddy/be an adder? If the plaid-clad caddy-laddie/addled daddy in his adding/ would the plaid-clad caddy-laddie's daddy/make the plaid-clad caddy-laddie sadder?

Now notice the puckered corners of your mouth in forming 'r' in:

(b) Around the rugged rock/the ragged rascal ran.

(c) And the tongue to teeth in:
Timothy Theocolus / Thwickham Thwack Thwacket/thrust his two thick thumbs/ through three thousand/three hundred/and thirty-three/thin and thick thistles/. Where are/the three thousand three hundred and thirty-three/thin and thick thistles/that Timothy Theocolus Thwickham Thwack Thwacket / thrust his two thick thumbs through?

As you recognise repetition of words, notice also that your mind is capable of expanding the phrasing. This is good training in gradually increasing speed, little by little from your first efforts.

2. Now a Nonsense Rhyme. (An alternative to this can be found among studies at the end of Part II.)

Concentrate only on the movement of 'b' on the lips.

BEES IN NOVEMBER

A bee, rather blousy, boomed in at my window.
Blodwyn they called her because of her bust.
She boomed and she banged and she bounced
    on the book-case,
And buzzed bitter curses in bouts of disgust.

She wore a fur coat: black, with bands of
    bright yellow.
Tortoise-shell specs on the bridge of her nose;
Buttoned-up boots; and her legs a bit bandy
Beamed beautifully bright in black silken
    hose.

Said I to my soul: Blodwyn teaches a lesson:
Though winter it be, don't be downcast and
    dumb.
Bedeck thy old body with bold bobbydazzlers;
Be blythe, and be bobbish, and make the
    world hum.

                      Edith Allen

"WHAT'S GOING ON HERE?"

Rosalie, born deaf, learns by the Play Way to lip-read and speak at one and the same time in a nursery class among children of her age with normal hearing.

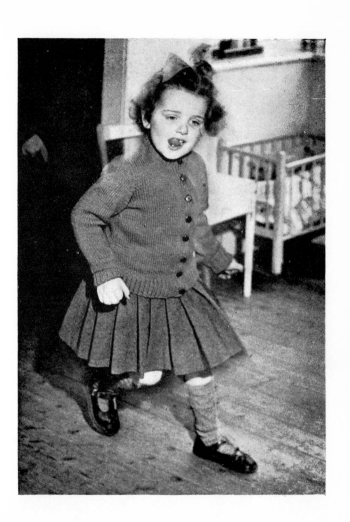

"PAUL, PAUL, LAY THE TABLE."

There is no doubt about it, Rosalie has lip-read her instructions. Her teacher, catching the eye of opportunity, calls across the room, "Rosalie, lay the table!" (There was no special attention to risk setting up self-centredness.) Rosalie sets to work, but calls "Paul, Paul, lay the table". She has been 'taught' nothing. She has taught herself in the usual nursery and kindergarten manner by 'Play Ways'. Having 'felt her way' into playing with hearing children, she is 'picking up their ways'.

She looks a little disappointed, however. that Paul thinks it his duty to pour the tea as well? But if this be true, it remained unsaid, for sentence-making in a 'fighting cause' has not yet materialised, and argument is out of the question! So peace prevails.

LESSON 2

About the Synthetic Method

THIS lesson explains more fully the Synthetic Method, which *I* think is a quicker and less formal method, and more fun than the analytical, but it also shows how necessary it is to be conscious of analysis to check up as you go along.

I found nothing *but* the analytical method (the letter-by-letter, sound-by-sound system) a strain and a 'panic'. In trying to interpret it, I experienced a sense of forever getting behind—of always trying to catch up, and, never doing it, thus developing a feeling of frustration and fatigue. And so I set to work to try to adapt the method I had been accustomed to using successfully when teaching ordinary young children to read, and I found the synthetic method of lip-reading enlivening, full of expectancy and mental adventuring; combining this with analysis when necessary, I felt interested and sure of my ground; and we must not forget that interest, not drudgery, at any age, is the key to progress and stimulates the love and will to work well.

The synthetic method aims at showing not so much

what to learn, but how to learn it, and I am going to give my first synthetic lesson just as I would to children, for we are children in the experience of lip-reading, as yet, so let us consider how they learn to read at school nowadays.

They learn to recognise the shapes of words, phrases, etc., on the printed page, as we shall learn to recognise the shapes of words on the speaking mouth. And if you are wise, you will use your mind's ears, and imagine the speaking voice behind the words, and you will watch the facial expression of the speaker to help that imagination to build up the impression of what is being said.

Now, before giving you the shapes of the words you are going to recognise, 'shake yourself loose', that is, relax, mind and body. That does not mean don't concentrate, but it does mean don't panic. It will come! It does with children if they practise every day, and it will with us if we are conscious of what we are trying to do. 'We can because we think we can' is not a bad creed for lip-readers.

What *are* we trying to do? Let us remind ourselves once more. We are looking for shape and movement in relation to sound, and we shall apply to our efforts some knowledge of the processes going on in the mind which help us to achieve our end.

Children learning to read begin with words— not letters—jolly words about things they know and love; picture words, which we shall call 'clue words' for our purpose (the nouns and verbs, which are the naming and doing words essential to the set-up of a sentence).

Here are the words, the shapes, that we are going to recognise:

rabbit nibbling grass

three word-shapes bringing to the mind of the child expectancy and the 'association of ideas' (a valuable principle in learning). The child's mind is ready at once to form the sentence: 'The rabbit is nibbling the grass.' He now has the 'shape' of the sentence as well (his mind has subconsciously anticipated the shape of the whole), and he gets a natural rhythm in saying it. The child is now ready for something more than 'The rabbit is nibbling the grass'. He is ready and expectant to expand the sentence, bit by bit, to the full form that is already in the mind of the teacher. Still being trained to recognise shape in the picture, or clue words, and to keep his mind alert to fill in new words, he arrives at it thus:

(1) Rabbit . . . . nibbling . . . . grass.

(2) The rabbit is nibbling the grass. Then two new words: 'little', 'green', and off we go again, over the old ground which helps us to absorb and assimilate —two other processes in learning—while still retaining the sense of expectancy.

(3) The little rabbit is nibbling the green grass. Two more new word-shapes; 'White', and 'fresh'.

(4) The little white rabbit is nibbling the fresh green grass. By this time the children will have gained a hold on this sentence, and it will help to relieve the fatigue and boredom of seeing the same, now well-organised, word shapes if we finish the sentence with two 'phrase-shapes':

pink ears   dewy lawn

and the sentence becomes:

The little white rabbit with pink ears is nibbling the fresh green grass on the dewy lawn.

Finally, they are asked, by way of 'association of ideas': 'What colour will you expect the white rabbit's eyes to be?' 'Pink eyes' is added, and the sentence, picturesque, powerful and rhythmical to the children's senses becomes: 'The little white rabbit/with pink ears and pink eyes/is nibbling/the fresh green grass/on the dewy lawn.

In working out this idea with adult, lone lip-readers, at the beginner's stage, a mistake in the interpretation of one of them showed us exactly what becomes necessary, both to ourselves and to hearing children at the same stage, i.e. analysis to check up synthesis. The student was severely deaf, but she had an alert mind, which jumped to a conclusion and to the gist of the matter, and she lip-read . . . 'nibbling the fresh green grass in the dewy meadow'—a good conclusion, but not the correct one. We had been working only on the Synthetic method. We now had to check up by using

the Analytical one. The one builds up to create the
live impression and interest; the other analyses, or
breaks up into the component parts to *check up* and
ensure the *right* impression. This is where we teach
the children the sounds of the letters. (See list of
sounds: Appendix 1.) It couldn't be meadow, which
begins with the sound of 'm'. The very fact of its
beginning with the sound of 'l' suggests 'lawn',
without boredom to the child whose mind is
associating sensibly: white rabbit, pet rabbit, lawn.

I said above that this method was practised out on
lone lip-readers. These felt that they were at a dis-
advantage, having no one with whom to practise.
But, you know, we have little mirrors into which we
can speak, noticing the shapes as we speak them
(and let us speak them clearly, as all good speakers
should). We also have the feel of them as we speak
them; and as we go along the road, with our thoughts
as companions, we can think of the shape and the
feeling of them in our mouths and on our lips, were
we forming them there. We can go further in our
practice. We can train ourselves to look objectively
at our own words in the mirror, as if they were
spoken by somebody else. In this way, synthesis and
analysis become slowly balanced up, and we reach
the stage when we do not know whether we are
hearing (if we have any hearing left) or lip-reading.
Actually we are doing both, and if we continue to do
so, we shall soon find that we have ninety per cent.

of our hearing back; and who really needs more than that? And if we train our eye just to pick out clue words, and our mind to fit in the 'with's, 'by's, 'of's, 'and's, and 'the's, and the little phrases that give rhythm, form and content to the sentence, with the clue words, we shall do it without fatigue, and we shall find ourselves becoming conversationalists as well.

Practice Work on Lesson 2

Recognising word shapes

1. Here are the word shapes that we are going to recognise:

        rabbit   nibbling   grass

2. Proceed as follows, speaking them into your mirror:

    (*a*) The rabbit is nibbling the grass.
        (And two new words: little, green.)

    (*b*) The little rabbit is nibbling the green grass.
        (Add: white, fresh.)

    (*c*) The little white rabbit is nibbling the fresh, green grass.
        (Add: pink ears, dewy lawn.)

    (*d*) The little white rabbit, with pink ears, is nibbling the fresh green grass on the dewy lawn.
        (Add: pink eyes.)

     (*e*) The little white rabbit, with pink ears and
               pink eyes, is nibbling the fresh green
               grass on the dewy lawn.

Thus your sentences are gradually extended, and
the repetition each time is making your recognition
of them automatic.

(3) Finally, find somebody to speak the whole
sentence to you. 'Translate it', so to speak, from the
words on the printed page to the words on the
speaking mouth. This is speech- or lip-reading.

*Further Suggestions and Examples of Self-help Practice
Methods: Extensions on Clue Words Associated
with the Playing-field*

Remember the purpose of these exercises by
familiarising a clue sentence around a clue word
(by repetition) to train the mind expansively towards
the whole by co-ordinating mind and eye in
associated ideas, extensions and retention.

Clue Word: BAT.
Clue Sentence: I'M GOING TO BUY A BAT.

   1. I'm going to buy a bat.
      I'm going to buy a bat and ball.
      I'm going to buy a bat and ball for my boy.
      I'm going to buy a bat and ball for my boy
         because it is his birthday.
      I'm going to buy a bat and ball for my boy,
         because it is his birthday next week.

Clue Words: BAT, TALL BOY, PLAYING-FIELD, POUNDS.

2. The bat will be a big one.

   The bat will be a big one, because my boy is a tall boy.

   For a tall boy the bat will cost about two pounds.

   For a tall boy, the bat will cost about two pounds, and the ball will cost about fifteen shillings.

   My boy will play with the bat and ball in the field.

   My boy will play with the bat and ball in the playing-field every evening.

   My boy will play with the bat and ball in the playing-field every evening after tea.

3. *In revising the whole*, as a whole, add some adjectives and make some variations, e.g.

I'm going to buy a big bat and a ball/for my eldest son/because it is his fifteenth birthday next week./The bat must be a large one/for Billy is a tall boy./The bat and ball will cost about two pounds fifteen/Billy and his friends will play cricket in the playing-field/every evening after tea.

Ask somebody to give you this as a dictation, phrased as shown here.

LESSON 3	*Spotting Clue Words*

SPOTTING clue words is quite an interesting practice, and makes for quick reception, so helpful when you are trying to "read" in conversation. Lesson 2 began with the clue word or subject "Rabbit" and the associated word shapes were "nibbling" and "grass", and on these three the whole of the descriptive sentence was built up.

In training oneself to read conversations, it is good practice in the early stages to sit back and try to pick out just the picture or clue words. If people know you are deaf—that is, with strangers, if you are bold enough to tell them—they will often be good enough to turn to you, and give you just the clue subject of the conversation: e.g. "We're talking about furniture for our new home." Your mind is then ready to associate various pieces of furniture with the subject and the rooms into which they will be put, and you will soon find yourself detecting a sentence here and there. "This morning we bought an oak table for the dining-room. The carpet there is fawn and brown." Here you may lose it, or take a rest. Presently you bestir yourself again. "Bed" you will see. "Spare-room", and with an anticipating mind, and a flash forward, without further ado, you have: "The bed in the spare-room is a Slumberland." On again: clue: "the blankets . . . and sheets . . . are still very expensive." And so on. Even if you can only pick up a little here and there, it will help you to join in with some relevant remarks, and the practice of spotting clue words will keep other people interested in you, and you interested in other people.

I was interested to hear of an old lady who had reached the third stage of womanhood, the 'simply wonderful' one. I had been told she was a perfect lip-reader, so I called upon her to find out her secret. She had never learned lip-reading, nor did she really lip-read very much. She picked out the clue words, and then monopolised the conversation, everybody listening attentively. When somebody else entered into it, and she lost the drift, or the subject changed, the friend with whom she lived saw that she had no clue, and just prompted her: "We're talking about 'So and so'," and off she went again. A very interesting and intelligent woman.

So, if you can get somebody to practise clue spotting with you, giving you a clue subject, e.g. *Word Guide** Book 1, follow there the words

* The *Guide Word Books* are published by Davis & Moughton Ltd., Birmingham, at about 10*d.* each. Each of the first 3 books prove useful for lone lip-readers' mirror practice.

associated with the subject given. Put them into conversational sentences, and build up between you a full conversation. Or do it by yourself, into your mirror, which will necessitate analysing why it is, and what it is, to some extent.

Practice Work on Lesson 3

'Spotting' Clue Subjects and Words

Look out for the repeated shapes of these words in the following:—

heart, inches, times, beats, tons, seventy, hundred, thousand.

Look out also for other numbers.

How many readers know/that the heart/is six inches long/and four inches in diameter;/it beats/ seventy times a minute/thirty-six million/seven hundred and twenty thousand times a year;/at each beat/two and a half ounces of blood/are thrown out/ making eight tons a day./During seventy years/the heart lifts/two hundred and four thousand/four hundred tons. (The oblique line shows the normal speech pauses, making as suitable a reasonable reduction of the length of the phrases to our stage as beginners. We must gradually practise lengthening them.)

More clue subjects and words are to be found in Books 1 to 4 in the series *Guide Word Work.**

---

* The *Guide Word Books* are published by Davis & Moughton Ltd., Birmingham. See also p. 44 for further comments.

Practise with a partner at your club, or with your friend's help practise as partners. Choose a subject and make a conversation about it, giving the clue subject clearly, but without exaggeration.

Remember: A lip-reader cannot speech-read unless the speaker shows shape and movement clearly and without exaggeration. Speech-training must be as careful as speech-reading. If you want to be sure that your partner can see what goes on behind as well as in front of your teeth, place the tips of your first finger into your cheeks, just where dimples may appear, just behind the canine teeth, where you can feel the first molars. What you can see of shape and movement in your own mouth is what you will look for in other people's.

Practise this technique in your mirror.

| **LESSON 4** | *Initial Consonants for Movement Letters* |

FROM a dictionary make some lists of words, say ten or twelve, with the same consonants (movements) at the beginning of each word. Thoroughly familiarise yourself with these movements in relation to their sounds, speaking them into your mirror, whether you have a partner or not.

It is good to make your own lists, for you then know what you are looking for in the movement of each initial consonant, which you choose; conscious that you are translating, so to speak, your movement into sound correctly.

Repeat the exercise looking for the shape of the initial vowel as it follows the initial movement, on the lines shown in Lesson 1, e.g. Try the on-the-lips movements: 'p', 'b', and 'm' looking the same, but so easily detected in their associated words in sentences. And 'f' and 'v' similarly. Pe/ni/tence, pan/to/mime, bli/ster, bu/tter/fly.

If you can easily do so, without destroying the nature of the word, finish the syllable with the vowel shape, and begin the next with the consonant movement, or combined movements, e.g. Compare pe/ni/tence with pan/to/mime—not pen/i/tence or pant/o/mime. (These shapes on the lips would look as absurd as they do written down.) Compare the combined movements in: bli/ster and bu/tter/fly. (You're not tempted to forget the SOUND of 'U' in UP and BUTTERFLY are you?)

Concentration is an art which you will find essential in lip-reading. As you go about, especially by yourself, concentrate for a period on some chosen aspect of your studies. Begin by noticing people's expression when speaking in a bus, for example. Try to gather something of their facial expressions and reactions. Begin to be selective and critical.

Look out for:

1. Those who speak fairly slowly.

2. Those who open their mouths sufficiently to show sufficient movement of the lips, and what goes on with the tongue behind them.

3. Choose those who are sitting in a good light.

4. Be sure of these matters also, in your own speech.

You see, there is something in the power of suggestion. When I had only just begun lip-reading, I found myself getting on famously with a girl serving me in a shop. As she handed me my parcel, I said to her: "You speak very clearly. Did you know I was deaf?" She replied: "I thought you might be. You were speaking very clearly yourself." So don't waste time over slovenly speakers if you can help it. In shopping, give yourself time to look round for those who enunciate well, and avoid immobile lips, mumbly mouths and expressionless faces. And don't forget that an expression of enthusiasm in your own eyes does much to create confidence between you.

The tambourines are already satisfied and relaxed.

Cymbals: "Any moment now boys!"

Drums (left covered) await their call for action from the conductor.

Johnnie, with his triangle, would have preferred to bash the tambourine, and the little girl with a 'clapper' (front right) is still a little uncertain how and when to use it, but can look and learn from her neighbour.

All in action and Johnnie's triangle still serving!

'Bashing' play is as good for all babies as it is essential for handicapped ones, especially the born deaf, whose special speech difficulties limit their vocabularies and self-expression more, at first, than those of children hearing and speaking normally. The 'bashing away' obviates a sense of frustration and avoids 'tantrums' and tensions that are the inevitable results of frustration.

Every child expresses his or her feelings in such pictures as on the opposite page and generally reveals an orderly discipline that comes through a sense of expectancy.

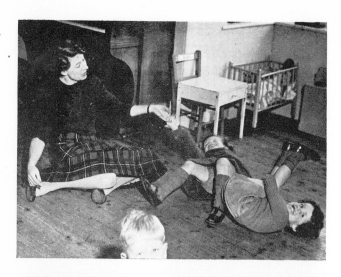

Another form of 'bashing' game is the romping one known at every party for the five-year-olds as "Atishoo, Atishoo, all fall down".

Every child loves it, and while using much energy, it also restores much, for it is a great reliever of tension in a special sense; it makes for self-forgetfulness and overcomes shyness, sensitiveness and boredom, from whatever cause they arise.

The ice is broken, the sense of being conspicuous has gone and 'the game is on'.

From their orderly circle-form the children disperse freely on the instruction: "Bunny jump".

Practice Work on Lesson 4

This poem will help you to study 'l', one of the sounds that it is not so easy to see.

A SONG OF LOVE
by Donald Hughes*

I love the full profusion of the earth
When spring's activities are brought to birth.
I love the summer's warm maturity
And mellow autumn's colour pageantry.
I love the charity of winter when
Peace and goodwill are witnessed among
    men. . . .

I love the ocean and I love the land.
I love a level stretch of silver sand.
I love the lapping wavelets and the roar
Of breakers as they crash upon the shore . . .

The linnet and the lark I dearly love.
I love the dunnock and I love the dove.
I love the blackbird who at dewy dawn
So handsomely perambulates the lawn . . .

* From *A Song of Love* in *Love and Laughter*, the collected poems of Donald Hughes, published by Rankin Bros. Ltd., Trenchard Street, Bristol.

I love the sound of laughter when it flows
Loudly and unreluctantly and shows
That hearts are happy, and I love the sound
Of sympathetic sorrow that is found
In soft and soothing sentences that show
An understanding note in times of woe.
I love good fellows who enjoy good food
And fellowship, and know that it is good.
I love the little girls and little lads
Who love their dinners and who love their
     dads.
I love the sight of bright young life about,
Not too tempestuous nor too shy to shout.
I love a lively lot of boist'rous boys
Who, though they make a maximum of
     noise,
Create, as well, a minimum of gloom
The moment that they burst into a room.

Does one good, doesn't it? I agree with the poet,
     There is enough to love in life today
     To make the whole community go gay!

Reading this poem will demonstrate to you the
movement of the protruding lips forming the sound
"ch".

from THE CHIPPENDALE CHAIRS
by Donald Hughes*

A dealer once bought a choice Chippendale
    chair
Made long years ago with meticulous care,
Excessively chaste and exceedingly rare.

A chair so enchanting had seldom been
    seen.
It was fit for a King to present to his Queen,
Or for an Archdeacon to offer his Dean.

Downstairs in his cellars the dark deed was
    done.
Eleven more Chippendale chairs were begun,
Antiquity characterising each one.

His spurious products were taken upstairs,
And soon, in his showroom with other old
    wares
There might have been seen "twelve choice
    Chippendale chairs . . ."

---

* From *The Song of Love,* by Donald Hughes.

LESSON 5

Association of Ideas

As you continue your study of speech-reading, you will find how valuable is the principle of 'Association of Ideas'—an extension of the spotting of clue words described in Lesson 3.

In listening to general conversation, when you have found, or been told, your clue: (e.g. "We're talking about kitchen gadgets that Mrs. X. is collecting") your mind at once sets to work suggesting a number of things in connection with it, and you find yourself recognising some of these by the shape and movement of the mouth you are watching, and you will find yourself building up the sentences around these words. You will find yourself getting the gist of what is being said, and be able, therefore, to take some relevant part in the conversation. This, too, will relieve the fatigue of lip-reading, for, as you take the initiative, you also give the clue, and so can follow it up in your own way.

You will find it helpful, also, to realise that the circumstances in which you find yourself readily associate themselves with the spoken words, as does also the rhythm of the speech. In this connection, I once interpreted a speech from two words—rabbit and fish.

A nurse was standing at the foot of a patient's bed, holding a plate, at dinner-time. These circumstances, the rhythm and the two words built up the following conversation:

Patient: What is it, Nurse?

Nurse: Rabbit.

Patient: Is there anything else? I don't like rabbit.

Nurse: There's fish.

Patient: Thank you, I'll have fish.

It is quite amazing, if you know these principles, and train your mind to work on them, how you 'get going'. At a lesson on Homophonous words (words which look alike) I was asked to interpret what I thought was the following sentence: "I had a telegram from Shanghai this morning." Pleased with myself at what I thought was a quick pick-up of the sentence, I began to reproduce it when my mind checked me. "Telegrams from Shanghai?" it said. "Cables from Shanghai." And, as quickly, the correct sentence came:— "I had a telegram from the Channel Isles this morning," the two names being similar enough, at the stage I had arrived at, to be thought homophonous.

Let me illustrate this principle of Association of Ideas by referring to a game our lip-reading group played at the club.

Sitting in a circle, a player suggests one word. Each in turn offers one word associated with the previous one. This sounds as if it would be very exacting for the memory, and it is, at first, being combined with lip-reading the words, but the repetition of the words is excellent practice, and eases the effort that is necessary.

The first player suggested DOG, and the game continued thus:—

dog	suggests	master
master		home
home		farm
farm		country
country		sheep
sheep		lambs
lambs		shepherd
shepherd		shepherding
shepherding		foxes
foxes		huntsmen
huntsmen		horses
horses		hounds
hounds		horn
horn		John Peel
John Peel		community singing

Then it was suggested that we should use some of these words as an essay, to be given as dictation, read from the lips, at the next lesson. It was read through normally once, to be heard by those who could be made to hear, in order to look for clue words. Then it was reread without hearing, in short phrases, rhythmically. It was then dictated, sentence by sentence or phrase by phrase, to be written, the oblique lines indicating the rhythm.

"The dog/follows his master/home to the farm./ The farm/is full of sheep and lambs./The shepherd/ guards the lambs/from the foxes./The foxes/are hunted by the huntsmen/and the hounds./The hounds follow the horn./The horn was played by John Peel./A song about John Peel/is a favourite for community singing."

As you improve and find yourself making progress, you can practise this mental training of spotting clue words as you listen to the wireless, especially with those who speak very fast. Notice only the clue words, and form a mental picture of how they look on the speaker's mouth. Do the same with the slower speakers. With these, though concentrating only on finding the clue words, you will presently become aware that your mind is conscious of the whole sentence, forming it, with the speaker, around the clue words. Do not 'try hard' to do it. It will soon come placidly with the slow speaker. The quick one will find you panicking—always trying to catch up, and maybe, finally, tired and frustrated, you give up.

But never get to that stage with your experiments.

| LESSON 6 | *Sequence in Associating Ideas* |

By this time, one hopes, you are realising that you are becoming lip-reading-conscious, and aware of what an interesting hobby it is to become. You may find yourself suddenly being struck by passages that you come across in your general reading which would make good and interesting practice for your lip-reading, because they bear out some of the principles which you have been studying, because they contain repetition of words for the practice of the eye in an interesting context of association for the practice of the mind. This combination of shape-hunting (analysis) and association (synthesis) will help your readiness and accuracy.

You will find yourself building up an anthology,

and, mysteriously enough, around your anthology
may grow up a companionship of those who may
practise lip-reading with you, at your club, or in the
closer companionship of your home. Then you will
find that your companionship is one of like-minded
people, and your contacts are widening generally,
and often delightfully unexpectedly. The association
of ideas, too, is widening in a most interesting
way.

Now, for our study, notice the association of
ideas in the serial sequence of the following practice
piece. It is part of a description in 'Sanatorium,'
to be found in *The Complete Short Stories of
Somerset Maugham.**

The oblique lines represent the simple, rhythmic
phrasing for your ease at this stage, and emphasise
the groups of words representing unfolding associations. The emphasis marks suggest the vowels
forming the shape on the mouth.

Practice Work

from Somerset Maugham's *There and Then*

Chester was a perfectly ordinary man,/somewhere
between thirty and forty,/married,/with two children./
He lived in a decent suburb. /He went up to the

* Published by Heinemann.

city every morning/and read the morning paper. /He had no interests except his business/and his family./ He liked his work;/and he made enough money/to live in comfort. /He put by a reasonable sum/every year. /He played golf on Saturday afternoons/and on Sundays. /He went every August for three weeks' holiday/to the same place/on the East Coast;/his children would grow up and marry,/then he would turn over his business to his son,/and retire with his wife/to a little house in the country/where he could potter about/till death claimed him/at a ripe old age.

Clue Sentence: 'CHESTER WAS A PERFECTLY ORDINARY MAN.'

Method.—Get a friend to read this passage to you— or read it into your mirror. Listen with as little volume of voice or hearing aid as possible—enough to keep your mind and eye relaxed as you watch the words and gather the unfolding associations. Then study the piece, phrase by phrase. Notice that these emphasis marks fall almost always on the *shape* letters. It would be worth while analysing this piece to discover how many of them are represented.

Complete your lists under these shape headings. Then lip-read them in your mirror.

e.g. *e*	*er*	*or*
Chester	perfectly	ordinary
every	thirty	forty
read		

u	*a*	*oo*
some	married	two
suburb		

ee	*i*	*ay*
decent	city	paper
reasonable	interest	made
	business	

oh	*ie*	*o*
no	liked	golf
coast	by	holiday

ah	*ou*	
afternoons	house	

From now on, every passage selected to initiate the practice lesson is in fact a potential dictation. No lesson should now be considered complete without a piece of dictation if it can possibly be arranged. (There are many passages suitable for dictation in Part II of this book, or you can choose your own.) At least a quarter of an hour should be spent in this way—it demonstrates your progress and your accuracy (or the lack of them!).

Anybody can give the dictation provided that he or she has and gives clear speech without affectations, which produce contortions of the mouth and are therefore confusing. School-children can be excellent helpers. They are *au fait* with the way their teachers phrase, and they are quick to apply suggestions.

The selected piece for this lesson has been phrased as it should be dictated. The helper should read it thus and make himself or herself 'at home' with it, so that both partners may be able to concentrate easily.

LESSON 7 | *Rhyme, Rhythm and Association of Ideas in relation to Concentration and Fatigue*

As you continue your practice and consciousness of shape and movement, become rhythm-conscious, noticing the phrasing of speech. If somebody were reading aloud at slow speed for the purpose of studying speech, this fact of rhythm would be all the more noticeable. You would notice, also, that there is a tendency to close the lips here and there in long passages. It is worthwhile noticing these pauses in the phrasing of speech, and being conscious of the rhythm that they make. It helps to reduce fatigue, to enhance concentration, and to obviate the sense of always trying to catch up.

Turn again to the practice work on Lesson 6 from *There and Then* by Somerset Maugham. You will find the descriptive essay phrased for the purpose. Read it aloud and feel the rhythm. Notice the pauses as you read them into your mirror.

I think the rhythm of poetry reading makes good practice at this stage. Conscious now of shape and movement, the very lilt of the rhythm will help you unconsciously to anticipate the rhyme, and so, again—but now unconsciously—emphasise shape and movement. "Couplets" (pairs of words that go together) and proverbs are also good training in the rhythm of speech.

Practice Work

A STUDY IN RHYME

Study the following rhyme from a similar point of view.

Clue Subject: THE FARMYARD

(This clue subject at once associates itself in my mind with a Devon farm I passed when motoring. It might be a description of the same farm. The oblique lines indicate the expansion of the clue phrases, which is at the heart of the synthetic method.)

One black horse/standing at the gate.

Two plump cats/eating off a plate.

Three big goats/kicking up their heels.

Four pink pigs/full of grunts and squeals.

Five white cows/coming slowly home.

Six small chicks/starting off to roam.

Seven fine doves/perched upon the shed.

Eight grey geese/eager to be fed.

Nine young lambs/full of frisky fun.

Ten brown bees/buzzing in the sun.

Notice that it will help your speed, repeatedly give you a good start, and reduce your fatigue to anticipate the numbers coming in sequence—the first word in each line—to anticipate the rhyme—the last word of the line; and to associate, as you often do, normally, thus:

"CHOOSE" GAMES

This is an excellent vocabulary-speech-training game. The teacher chooses the children by name, one by one to come out and choose a toy. Conversely the teacher names the toys of her choice.

The first real thrill for Rosalie's teacher came when Rosalie left her place, went to her teacher and said quite clearly, "Choose me". Short instructions for each try followed and 'sentence building' began.

There was no doubt about the efficiency of such a game in her connection. Not only was she alert and expectant for her turn to choose, but in watching for her name's shape on the teacher's mouth, she saw similarly other children's names shaped there, Paul's (an easy one) no doubt among them.

Without teaching or theorising, Rosalie had fallen upon a principle: 'Put your breath behind the shapes on the mouth and something will come'.

'WONDER'

Rosalie is now not only talking in her waking hours but in her sleep. Thus though she hears nothing, the shape and movement on the mouth are meaning something—meaning the 'picture things' she sees the experiences she is having of doing things.

I would call this picture 'wonder'.

The children are acting (mime) the story of "The Sleeping Beauty". The hundred years' spell is broken and the Sleeping Princess is awakened by the prince and claimed as his bride-to-be.

Rosalie does not know the story yet, of course, but nevertheless, the 'Expectancy' habit, already forming, reveals itself as progressive in WONDER.

horse—standing—gate

cats—eating—plate

goats—kicking—heels

pigs—grunts—squeals

cows—coming—home

small—chicks—roam

doves—perched—shed

grey—geese—fed

lambs—frisky—fun

bees—buzzing—sun

Such natural, picturesque associations.

RHYTHMIC 'COUPLETS'

Aim.—To train the mind's acceptance of rhythm in speech; concentration; relaxation through that acceptance; and the readier recognition of the shape in the clue words and the flow of the sentence-building which the rhythm enhances.

Bread and butter	Moon and stars
Son and heir	Feet and hands
Veal and ham	Pots and pans
Pepper and salt	Cart and horse

Hot and cold

Winter and summer

Male and female

Black and white

Ups and downs

Heads and tails

Sow and reap

Dig and delve

Ducks and drakes

Soul and body

Cup and saucer

Light and darkness

Hill and dale

Time and tide

Sage and onions

Soap and water

Safe and sound

Needles and pins

Hither and thither

Young and old

Whisky and soda

Stuff and nonsense

Fish and chips

Lover and lass

Bubble and squeak

Boy and girl

Watch and chain

Liver and bacon

Brush and comb

Long and short

Cream and jam

These can be added to *ad lib*.

It is a good and simple practice also, at your club-reading, to ask your leader to give you the first half of the 'couplet' as clue word practice, and for you to supply the complete 'couplet' for rhythm. These 'couplets' or word-pairs come easily to your mind, because they are rhythmic and familiar.

Thus you find yourself alert and relaxed at one and the same time, and able to check up shape and movement.

Work on some proverbs with the same sense of balance, rhythm and completion.

Partners give the first half of the proverb, as practice in 'spotting clue words', allowing the other partner to provide the whole couplet from it.

A bird in the hand/is worth two in the bush.

A friend in need/is a friend indeed.

A rolling stone/gathers no moss.

A stitch in time/saves nine.

A thing of beauty/is a joy for ever.

All's well/that ends well.

Birds of a feather/flock together.

God helps those/who help themselves.

Nothing venture/nothing gain.

What's sauce for the goose/is sauce for the gander.

The early bird/catches the worm.

Spare the rod/and spoil the child.

The proof of the pudding/is in the eating.

There's many a slip/'twixt the cup and lip.

What can't be cured/must be endured.

Add to these proverbs for yourself. They are a great source of supply for rhythm. They form sentences of controlled length for your practice alone.

| **LESSON 8** | *Absorption and Assimilation* |

THESE are principles which aid your memory and help you to keep hold of what you have learned. They are closely linked with some aspects of the psychology of the hard of hearing. Learning to apply them emphasises once again how necessary it is to combine synthesis and analysis if one is to get full value from either or both. Some do this more naturally than others.

ABSORPTION is that process which takes place when the material being studied enters and becomes part of your conscious mind. You 'digest' it, so to speak.

ASSIMILATION takes place when the material being studied becomes a part of yourself. Having entered the sub-conscious mind from the conscious, it is there 'pigeon-holed' for return to and use through the conscious mind which recalls it from the sub-conscious mind as association of ideas when occasion demands. It has become a part of your bloodstream, as it were.

In the ordinary way, if we concentrate normally, these two processes come automatically. With the hard of hearing, however, the mind accepts and registers less easily and readily, and therefore more superficially, owing to the nature of the disability itself, and to fatigue which makes for greater difficulty in concentrating.

A few minutes well spent with your mirror each day on shape and movement drills from the books recommended* for the purpose will help to make these processes easier. Remember, too, some dictionary work on initial movement letters in words. Work at them now systematically, turning to the initial letters of words in your dictionary in the order in which your chart gives them (Appendix 1). Thus you will continue to be impressed with the movement of initial consonants together with initial vowel shapes which give a strong clue to the whole word and which, together with the principle of association, or context, are so absolutely essential to the set-up of lip-reading, and the success of the lip-reader.

As you finish your approach to lip-reading on

* *Guide Word Books*, Davis & Moughton Ltd., Birmingham. (See Lesson 3).

the synthetic method, you will begin to realise that each lesson has some connection with absorption and assimilation, and the daily life they help you to lead as a handicapped person. Panicky concentration makes them practically impossible. Aim at lip-reading with relaxation.

The consciousness of rhythm welling up towards the slight pauses which lightly emphasise clue words also helps to relieve the strain of concentration, so enhancing the chances of absorption and assimilation—the partners and supporters of memory. Rhythm, as you began to learn in the last lesson, is indeed the music of lip-reading, as it is of speech. It means to lip-reading what all the rallentandos and the various nuances of musical composition mean to music. And the study of it, of course, increases one's sensitiveness to it. Just so is this the case with those who have the good fortune to lip-read with somebody with the love and patience to give to the daily study of it. Even at anything less than the best, it can be an indispensable help. (I know this from experience.)

Then let impression and expression work together when you can. Sometimes write down what you have heard, so that it will be more deeply impressed, and will relax the strain on the memory. By doing this openly, as it becomes necessary in everyday life, we shall gain courage, and in accepting instead of trying to hide the inevitable from ourselves and others, our handicap will have a positive, instead of a negative influence upon our characters and our contacts.

This writing-down aspect of the study can well be broadened; try making lip-reading anthologies from your general reading. With the picture of the whole in your mind's eye, and the *study* in your mirror of some selected passage that appeals to you, you will have absorbed and assimilated something worth keeping. "Then", as Mary Webb says: "if life is suddenly simplified by the removal of all we hold most dear, we shall know the way to other things, not less precious . . . that will lead us into peace."*

Practice Work

ABSORPTION AND ASSIMILATION

Just work away at your drills, making up your mind and choosing what, especially, you are looking for—e.g.

1. Word building from dictionaries and *Guide Word* or other suitable spelling books.

   (*a*) Looking only for the initial letter which gives clue *movement* to the word.

* *The Spring of Joy* by Mary Webb. Published by Jonathan Cape.

(*b*) Looking only for the letter giving an initial clue *shape* to the word.

2. Recognising the initial word as you build on syllables and become conscious of the rhythm the syllables make—e.g.

rain, rainy, raining, rainbow, rainfall

3. Recognise rhythm in selected longer words from your dictionary. Try to see the first syllable and accented ones as clue to the rhythmic word— e.g. re/mem/ber, in/duce/ment, sim/pli/city, li/ bra/rian.

Say them several times to yourself until you feel you are absorbing the idea that you are working at, and assimilating the word that is 'working itself in' by your absorption of the shape, movement and rhythm you have elected to notice.

LESSON 9 | *Words that Look Alike on the Speaking Mouth (Homophonous Words)*

WORDS that look alike on the speaking mouth and sound alike when voiced, e.g. ball and bawl, are called Homophonous Words. But each has a different meaning. Some groups contain a dozen or more such words. Now let us see how our Synthetic Method can be applied to them.

Here, for example, is a group of nine homophonous words. Speak them into your mirror, and see that they do look alike:

dew, due, do, too, two, to, gnu, new, knew

There is little chance of mistaking their meanings if you can lip-read these sentences which contain them.

1. I knew you would be late for church.

2. There was a heavy dew on the grass this morning.

3. I want you to do me a favour.

4. Do you know an animal called the gnu?

5. If you buy too cheap a carpet it will not **wear** well.

6. How much is due for the milk account this week?

7. Two boys stole apples from my garden this morning.

8. I bought a new hat at the sales this week.

9. I must go to bed now.

Exercise 1

With the nine words written in front of you, get a friend to read the sentences in order, giving you clearly the number of each sentence. Place the appropriate number of the sentence over the homophonous word that you are on the look-out for—e.g., having lip-read and got the sense of sentence 2, place its number with an arrow over 'dew', thus

as no other word would be appropriate for that sentence.

Exercise 2

Try to fit words looking like 'died' into the following sentences, and speak them into your mirror:

(e.g. The man *died* from appendicitis)

1. I must have my blue dress —— this spring.

2. The children can bathe at low ——.

3. I've —— a knot in my shoe-lace.

4. The wireless says there will be a frost to ——.

5. My father has been made a ——.

6. —— and one make ten.

7. My new shoes are too ——.

This kind of practice will give you conversational confidence in recognising the right homophonous word, simply by means of its context.

Solution to Homophonous Words Exercises

Exercise 1

2	6	3	1	4	7	5	9	8
↓	↓	↓	↓	↓	↓	↓	↓	↓
dew	due	do	knew	gnu	two	too	to	new

Exercise 2

1. dyed
2. tide
3. tied
4. night
5. knight
6. nine
7. tight

| LESSON 10 | *Techniques for Ease and Flexibility in Speech* |

PRACTISE these sentences and phrases as used in ordinary conversation.

e.g.

1. How long will you be in the bathroom?
2. How much money did he leave in his will?
3. How many of your fowls are laying each day?
4. How much have you paid for coal this winter?
5. How soon do you expect your son home from Germany?

6. Which have you brought with you, a trunk or a suit-case?

7. Where have I to put the groceries, please?

Add words to the following to make sentences.

e.g.

1. Wouldn't you . . . (prefer to sit in the front of the car?)

2. Haven't we . . . (had a lovely day for our picnic?)

3. Shan't we . . .

4. Won't we . . .

5. Doesn't she . . .

6. Can't they . . .

7. Don't you . . .

8. Mustn't he . . .

9. Shouldn't they . . .

10. Oughtn't we . . .

etc.

Then look out for these forms in sentences a friend or practising partner may compose for you. Help her in the same way.

1. I'll

2. I'm

3. I've

4. He's

5. He'll

6. He'd

7. She'd

8. She'll

9. She's

10. We'd

etc.

Try others for yourself, placed in sentences of your own making; speak them into your mirror if you are working alone.

Notice such shortened forms common in everyday speech as they are applied in the next lesson.

LESSON 11 | *A Conversation Piece*

INTERVIEWING A GARDENER
(Questions and answers make good practice
for partners.)

Master: Good morning. Your name is Brown?

Gardener: David Browne, Sir. Browne with an E.

M. What is your age, Mr. Browne?

G. Browne will do, Sir. I'm seventy-five.

'TRIAL AND ERROR'

Rosalie has bitten her drinking straw, and her little friend has bent his, but they are already gaining a healthy independence. They will no doubt presently explore the way to relieve the embarrassing situation together first—before running to their teacher for help if they must. Such is the normal routine. "Try yourself first".

For a while, Rosalie abandoned the display of her "maternal instinct" in favour of structural play with bricks, but a sunny morning returned to her a 'young mother' activity.

Rosalie calls to Paul to join in a game of 'Mothers and Fathers'.

'SPEECH DAY AT A GIRLS' GRAMMAR SCHOOL'

"Three cheers for the Headmistress, the Staff and the School". Some of these girls are saying "Hurrah" and some "Hurray"! If in doubt, look for the shadows on the tongues. We do not do this consciously. It is what I mean, among other things, when I say "It will come". You can detect it in this picture: the narrow mid-tongue shadow in a groove for 'ay'; the spread one at the back of the tongue for 'ah' and the wide open mouth for 'ah' and puckered corners for 'ay'.

M. How long do you expect to go on practising as a gardener, Browne?

G. I don't expect to go on practising as a gardener, Sir. I've worked as a lover of gardens.

M. That's interesting. It sounds as if you might suit me. I'm not fond of foremen-gardeners.

G. Then I think you might suit me, Sir, and I might suit you.

M. Tell me, Browne, where have you worked?

G. Lord Wharton would give me a reference, Sir, or Sir Richard Ington, and I could tell you a little bit about a garden that I kept going for my old lady.

M. Go ahead. I'm not Lord Wharton, nor Sir Richard.

G. Well, Sir. It took me five years to find out that my little old lady wasn't as fussy as she seemed. She wouldn't let me dig deep. She wouldn't let me clear out the beds properly. She stopped me putting down poison for snails—in their hundreds, Sir—because it would poison the birds. She wouldn't let me plant young seedlings because the snails got them overnight. She wouldn't let me manure the ground properly because it meant deep digging.

M. Poor old soul! What did she have in her garden?

G. 'Twas the prettiest garden you ever met, Sir. And she knew everything that was in it by name. I'll tell you how it happened. She made me turn over the topsoil, and then wriggle my fork down until I felt the stones. She said the salts of the earth were there, and must stay there. Plenty of air could get down that way, she said.

M. Very good. Go on, Browne, to the snails.

G. I had to pick them up with my fingers, by the shells, and toss them on to the middle of the lawn. Now and then I'd give them a quick death under the spade, or the lawn mower. It brought the birds in scores, all around me in a few minutes —and a clean finish to the snails.

M. But how about the fruit trees, Browne?

G. She knew all about them too, Sir, and pruned them herself. Knew the birds that visited them —enjoyed the thought that buds were plentiful, even if bullfinches were as well.

M. Remarkable old lady. What age woman was she?

G. About my age, Sir. And believe it or not—she was BLIND.

M. Carry on, Browne. You'll do. Start on Monday, and long life to you.

G. Thank you very much, Sir. Am I going to get any pay? It's my hobby, of course, Sir, but a pensioner likes his pipe of an evening.

M. God bless my soul, Browne! You mustn't be such an interesting fellow. Ask what you like.

G. Quite content to leave it to you, Sir.

M. Good for you, Browne. That'll be all right.

G. Thank you, Mr. Rose, Sir. I'll be up by nine o'clock on Monday. Good morning, Sir.

Comments and "Homework"

This will make a good dictation and lip-reading exercise, taken a little at a time, as you and your partner decide. Dramatise it in your mind. Form your mental picture of it. When you have finished with it as a dictation, write an essay from it, absolutely free-style, describing the picture you have in mind of the old lady's garden, with herself and gardener consulting in it. This essay will of course be narrative, not dialogue (compare the passage given in Lesson 6). Then give your essay as dictation to your partner.

So you become a teacher as well as a learner. In this way you best learn to know what you are doing and what you can do, with lip-reading and its application to conversation. And what you took up as a hobby and a defence will help you to help those others who, seeing your success, will come to you for inspiration.

LESSON 12	*Students Express their Difficulties*

USE the "Questions and Answers" that follow as practice passages.

Clue Subject: HOW TO TACKLE YOUR DIFFICULTIES

1. "I just can't make anything of it."

"Oh yes you can! As you watch your teacher's or partner's moving mouth in her short, slow sentences, phrases or words, copy it as nearly as you can. Then again, put breath behind that shape and movement—that is, 'speak the shape'—well and boldly. Feel it coming. As nearly as you copy the words correctly the words will come correctly. They did so with an adult friend of mine, registered as born deaf, who had never spoken. By this method she read aloud, in a sweet, silvery voice. Her lip-movements were beautifully formed. Form yours in the mirror, beautifully, first silently, then voicing the words."

2. "I can hear what my partner is saying."

"Why shouldn't you? We are not asked to lose what hearing we have, but to support it with lip-reading. With what hearing you have you can check up the shape and movements with the actual sound of the words. Nowadays we teach reading and writing as one subject to hearing children—what they can read they can write, and vice versa. *We* are learning that what we can see on the lips we can say. Interpreting lip-reading comes with practice if you are conscious of *how* you are learning. Use your hearing aid to learn the fundamentals, then gradually reduce its volume so that finally you are interpreting only from what you see."

3. "I have no one with whom to practise."

"Use your imagination as you go about. Pretend you don't know your way to the Post Office; ask somebody, and check up the shape of the words on their mouth with what you already know!

"Don't be afraid to talk to people as you sit with or by them out of doors or in a bus. Tell them you are a little deaf. This will help them to adjust their speech to your hearing, and you to adjust the volume of your hearing aid to their speech.

"Practising the use and variation of volume and tone on your hearing aid is very important.

"Think your own thoughts as you walk the quiet ways, and think too what they would look like if you were speaking. Feel their shape and movement in your imagination.

"Have family suppers with yourself—invite photographs of your relations and friends to a meal. Make conversation with each photograph—make it into your mirror, and think of the mouth in your mirror as belonging to the friend with whom you are conversing.

"It's wonderful how flexible you can make your mind become to supply your needs."

4. "I can't cope with invisible initial letters."

"Just remember that they exist: c, g (hard as in gate), h and k. Think of the shape and movement of the word as a whole, and of the sentence as a whole. You'll soon find that 'Let's go 'ome' means 'Let's go home'. A more difficult one: 'We'll have cold lunch. I'm too busy to 'oo' today' ('I'm to busy to cook today'). The sense of the word rather than the word itself will just fit into the context of the whole sentence.

5. "I have no need to learn lip-reading now that I have a hearing aid."

"You'll be wise to. Now is the time to learn, against the time of increasing deafness, the drowning of words by background noises in the street, or the distance of a speaker who is too far away for you to hear. The hearing-aid-lip-reading combination is invaluable. It is estimated that it can give you 90% of 'hearing' if you persevere, and work, conscious always of what you are doing—until one day you realise that it is coming without conscious effort."

6. "I miss teaching when I can't get it."

"There's no need to. Do be your own teacher

on the lines I have advised. Make your own exercises and studies, using words, phrases and letter units you particularly want to study. You probably know your own difficulties as well as your teacher does. In the long run, we have to develop our art by ourselves. And lip-reading is not learned in the conventional twenty lessons."

7. "How should I study a completely new passage on my own?"

"I do beg you to practise the part from the whole. Aim at getting the gist of the whole by reading rapidly through the sentence, paragraph or anecdote. Get what you can of it by lip-reading it immediately afterwards. Get it complete and accurate by studying the words about which you are in doubt, and fitting them correctly into the whole.

"Never mind if you are 'remembering', as you say. You are also checking up your accuracy of shape and movement in relation to sound as you practise it in your mind."

8. "How can I keep my approach to lip-reading fresh?"

"Be interested in the inter-action between your conscious and subconscious minds. Don't dwell on your mistakes, but make them good in your mirror, and leave your mind to absorb and assimilate the correct version. An exercise-book record of the progress of your hobby will add interest, and a diary of any events at which you find yourself able to be 'lip-reading conscious'."

*　　　*　　　*

NOTE: The National Institute for the Deaf, 105, Gower Street, London, W.C.1., will always supply information, and send their magazine *The Silent World*, on application. Your Local Authority will also supply information.

PART II

INTRODUCTION TO PART II

THE first part of this book suggested how lip-reading can be approached in an informal way by those who must start in later years or who live alone. This second part suggests self-help methods and material. You can use the pages that follow both for dictation with your partner and for mirror-practice when you are alone.

Having arrived at lip-reading consciousness, one finds the hobby spirit entering into the study of it, and into the recognition of material for it. One soon begins to assess one's own needs and progress, and finds oneself selecting passages, articles, poems, purposefully, from the lip-reading-material point of view. The choice of the material becomes a most enjoyable part of one's 'hobby', whether it is being worked out for oneself, for sharing with a partner, or for a group at a club. Keep the hobby spirit in your practice, but remember that your progress will depend on how much time and opportunity you have, or can make, for practice, just as it does with those who learn to read the printed page, or a foreign language, or music.

The following pages are just suggestions as they have come along in the general reading and everyday incidents in the life of one who dwells alone, and must practise alone. Other enthusiasts in various stages of deafness have joined her, however, and either as severely deafened or as moderately hard-of-hearing people we know what a great help lip-reading can be, combined with what hearing we have. Those who live with others, too, will find an ability to lip-read, even a little, to be a great help, as it relieves the strain on both the hard-of-hearing and those who talk to them.

My 'anthology' may seem to you to be just a hotch-potch jumble. But each selection illustrates points to look for in your own material or ways of finding it. And, besides being very suitable for practice purposes, all these passages together have brought to me a message of hope, that no one needs to be lonely or afraid and that, whatever our cirstances, we are all capable of growing in grace.

*Suggestions for Self-help Methods
and Material*

THE LONELY DONKEY

HERE are one or two examples of how one can practise by oneself, using a mirror. They come from a recommended book: *The Lonely Donkey*, published by Wills and Hepworth, Ltd., Loughborough.

This is a delightful story about Ned, a little grey donkey who, though very lonely, tried to overcome his loneliness.

Many of his farmyard friends are far too busy to help him, but eventually he finds happiness and companionship with Timothy, a lonely little boy, through the advice and help of a wise old owl and a magpie.

(Notice the fairly easy movement of the lips in the following passage, as seen in words beginning with the 'clue' letters: w, wh, ch, sh, j. Contrast these with 's', lips drawn back.)

After a little time he reached the edge of the cliff, and looked down at the sea.

"What a lot of water," he thought. "How blue

'A CHRISTMAS CAROL PRACTICE'

"Nowell, Nowell, Nowell, Nowell,
Born is the King of Israel."

Shape and movement in relation to sound again. And for the dumb, who have never known sound: "Make your *shape* and the movement with it correctly, put your breath behind it, and 'something' will come. The *right* shape will bring the right sound."

Facial Expression is important for the deaf; first impressions of 'tone and attitude' value are very important as clues and reactions through the power of suggestion. By reacting to facial expression and expressive mannerisms they would become easily absorbed into the company, while finding more detailed clues through Lip-reading on the synthetic method. The picture expresses joy and enthusiasm in the singing of a merry song.

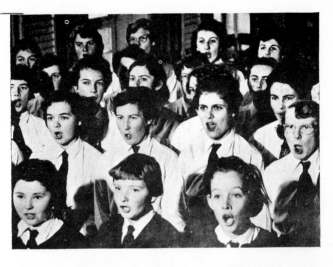

'LATE BEGINNERS'

The old lady conscientiously carries out the instructions. "Read the book right through first" (still in typescript) while she waits for the kettle to boil. Mirror practice was similarly applied from her hand-bag's 'vanity mirror', after following the first instructions.

'SPIRITUAL NEEDS OF THE AGED HOUSE-BOUND'

The Vicar regularly looks after the spiritual needs of the lonely, invalid and house-bound deaf.

Though extremely deaf she is able to follow the familiar words of the shortened form of the Communion Service for invalids.

it is." Then he saw the yellow sand, and the children playing and paddling.

"It looks very pleasant," said Ned out loud: and a sea-gull, overhearing them, said: "It is, you know."

Ned was going to answer him when he suddenly forgot all about the sea, and the sands and the sea-gull, for he had seen a little group of donkeys just below him.

"My goodness, those are donkeys like me!" he said. "Perhaps they'll let me stay with them, and then I'll never be lonely again," and he found a crooked little path, and made his way down to the shore.

(Continue the story contrasting the easily seen initial letter 'b' with the invisible letters 'c', 'g', and 'h'.)

But the donkeys laughed at him because he came from the country and knew nothing about sea-side donkeys' lives. They told him he could give the next ride, and see how he liked it, so a very fat, almost grown-up boy climbed on to his back, and he started off. How heavy the boy was, and how hot and uncomfortable the sand was: so different from the cool grass on the hill. The other donkeys laughed again when he got back, tired and out of breath. They told him he would never make a sea-side donkey, and they turned their backs on him and talked among themselves.

(Now look for the letters in the middle of words making the sounds of 'oo' and 'ee', with their accompanying shapes on the mouth.)

Ned got up and he and the magpie went down the hill and through the fields together. Ned trotted briskly and the magpie flew beside him. After a time they came to a road, and in the road were some large iron gates.

"You must go through these," the magpie said.

"Through these? But where are you taking me?" Ned asked, feeling very puzzled.

"You'll soon see," was all the magpie said in reply, and they went up a long drive with flowering bushes on either side, and green lawns beyond. And then, as they went round the bend, they met a man wheeling a wheelbarrow.

(Read the same passage again looking for 'oo', 'o', and 'ow' sounds, shaped on the mouth. Notice that other combinations of letters also say 'o' as in 'road'. Notice also 'ou' as in 'round' and 'ough' as in 'through'.)

"Hey you!" he called out, taking hold of Ned by his mane, "turn round and go out again, little donkey, you don't live here, you know," and he led Ned all the way back to the big gates.

"I don't like putting you out in the road, old chap," he said, "but I expect you'll soon find your way home," and he led the little donkey through and closed the gates behind him.

NOTE: I suggest this book as useful for adults as well as for children and their co-operative parents. The print is large and the spacing good for mirror practice for lone work or for speech work for couplet practice.

<table>
<tr><td>

LESSON

2

</td><td>

Recognising Repeated Words

</td></tr>
</table>

"SNIFFED OUT"

Exercise

Corned beef was sent to a Bridgend school canteen. Teachers sniffed it and did not like it. A canteen manageress sniffed it, but pronounced it good; the town sanitary inspector sniffed it but pronounced it good too; the town medical officer sniffed it and passed it as good—then ordered it to be destroyed because too many people had sniffed it.

Comment

As you read your papers, notice when word shapes, letter shapes or letter movements are often repeated. This consciousness will register on your mind, and you will find recognition becoming automatic all the sooner. Look, for instance, at the number of times the shape of 'i' comes in the above paragraph. Here it is in order of appearance: 'i' as in 'it'.

Bridgend sniffed did sniffed sanitary inspector sniffed it it medical officer sniffed it it sniffed it

Read it into your mirror now, and notice the shape of the word 'sniffed' wherever it occurs.

| **LESSON** **3** | *The Recognition of Repeated Words and Phrases* |

A Mystic's Story
by Meister Eckhart

THERE was a learned man who, for eight long years, desired that God should show him a man who would teach him the truth. And once, when he felt a very great longing, a voice from God came to him and said:

"Go to the church, and there thou shalt find a man who shall show thee the way to blessed-ness."

And he went thence and found a poor man whose feet were torn and covered with dirt and dust, and all his clothes were hardly worth three farthings. And he greeted him, saying:

"God give you good day."

He answered: "I have never had a bad day."

"God give you Good Luck."

"I have never had bad luck."

"May you be happy. But why do you answer me thus?"

"I have never been unhappy."

"Pray explain to me, for I cannot understand it."

The poor man answered: "Willingly. What God gives me, or ordains for me, be it good or ill, I take it cheerfully from God, as the best that can be, and so I have never had bad luck. You wished that God would make me happy. I was never unhappy: for my only desire is to live in God's will, and I have so entirely yielded myself to God that what God wills, I will."

"But if God should cast you into hell," said the learned man. "What would you do then?"

"Cast me into hell? His goodness forbids: But if He *did* cast me into hell, I should have two arms to embrace Him. One arm is true humility; that I should lay beneath Him, and be thereby united to His holy humility. And with the right arm of love, which is united with His holy divinity, I should so embrace Him that He would have to go to hell with me. And I would rather be in hell and have God, than be in heaven and not have God."

Then the master understood that true abandonment, with utter trust, is the nearest way to God.

"What brought you to this state of perfection?"

"My silence, my deep thinking and my union with God. For I could not rest in anything that was less than God. Now I have found God—and in God I have eternal rest and peace."

| **LESSON 4** | *Expansion: Reading Letters* |

Listen:

A postcard might be called a 'basic letter'.

A letter may be regarded as 'conversation on paper'. (A useful way of teaching an adult dumb person to speak who has learned only to read silently, and to lip-read without speech. They should be taught together.)

Here is the postcard. It has just arrived.

Bournemouth,
Easter Monday.

Many thanks for letter. Will reply soon after I get home. Glad all is going well with you. Can quite imagine the woods you visited.

Enjoying staying here—up to a point. Would rather be in Torquay.

Spent fine succession of evenings at the Winter Gardens. Delightful.

J.

Here is the letter which might have been written instead.

My dear Mabel,

Many thanks for your long letter. I am staying at Bournemouth for a few days. I will reply to your letter as soon after I get home as possible.

I am glad to hear that all is going well with you, and that you are enjoying yourself. I can quite imagine how lovely the wood must be where you had lunch on Friday—primroses, violets, wood anemones, cuckoo flowers and celandines. What a carpet of spring flowers of delicate colours, among the green grass.

I am enjoying my stay here—up to a point—but I would rather be in Torquay, with its greater variety of scenery, and many friends.

I spent a fine succession of evenings at the Winter Gardens. The music and the setting are delightful.

Yours very sincerely,
John Popman.

| LESSON 5 | *Newspaper Topics* |

CHRISTMAS FOOD FOR BRITAIN

Listen:

Ships from all parts of the world, laden with Christmas cargoes, docked at British ports before Christmas.

Warehouses on the London Docks were crammed with meat, fruit, butter and eggs. There were sacks of nuts, figs and dried fruits for the Christmas puddings, desiccated coconut and tins of fruit and syrup.

From Jamaica have come 50,000 tons of bananas. From New Zealand, dockers unloaded 167 tons of meat; 161 tons of butter; and 1,000 tons of cheese. Meat came also from Australia, South America, Denmark and Ireland.

Large consignments of mistletoe came from Northern France. Southampton docked nearly 50,000 crates.

Look out for:—

Names of countries.
Names of Christmas commodities.
Numbers.
Association of ideas.

D•

LESSON 6 | *Aims at Accuracy*

MY MOTHER'S ROMANCE

Exercise

My mother was always happy and gay, but she was not beautiful. She had, however, a most lovely voice. It won her many admirers. Among them was the professor who trained her. There was also Albert, who was poor, but very much in love with her.

The Professor, too, was in love with my mother. He promised her the height of her ambition as a singer. Albert could only offer her his love.

My mother's parents favoured the Professor. My mother said she would make her choice on the merits of their love.

She was going to sing at the Albert Hall and she knew that both her suitors would send her flowers. She promised her love to the one whose flowers she wore.

The Professor sent a beautiful bouquet of orchids. Albert sent rosebuds.

Flushed with the joy of love and of song, she took the platform wearing the red roses.

My mother is still alive at eighty-two, but Albert died at the age of sixty-five. When he died, a part of Mary (my mother) died with him, for theirs was a life-long romance.

(An original contribution)   M. Giles.

Comment

Try part or all of this, for the sake of accuracy, as a dictation.

1. Read it yourself, in print.
2. Translate it from the lips.
3. Write it from speech.

Accept it just as it is, trying to get the 'flow' of the story without any attempt at analysing shape and movement.

LESSON 7	*Shape, Movement and Rhythm*

RELATING EXPERIENCES IN THE COUNTRY

Clue Subject: WAS THE MAGPIE DEFENDING HER YOUNG?

Read the complete essay.

People attending school sports saw a hawk and a magpie circling round. The magpie was usually seen flying immediately above the hawk. Every now and then it dropped, apparently to attract the hawk, yet it appeared to be embarrassed by the hawk, not the hawk by it. This continued for over five minutes. Then the magpie made off, followed by the hawk, both dropping fast as if an attack might take place on the ground. About five minutes later, however, the hawk again appeared, with the magpie, flying upwards towards what appeared to be a second hawk though this one took no active part. The performance continued as before, without tragic results. But when the sky cleared, a magpie settled down on the branch of a tree, overlooking the crowd on the field of observation.

The question arose: Were the birds pairs? Was the attacking magpie defending her young?

(Study the initial shape and movement (vowels and consonants) in the following words, and as they appear elsewhere in the words.

'*a*' as in	'*e*' as in	'*i*' as in
appearing	embarrassed	ink
attack	every	if
apparently	second	it
again	settled	immediately
active	however	flying
magpie	when	continued
tragic		minutes
		with
		tragic

'*o*' as in   '*u*' as in
on   upwards
off   result
observation
continued
dropped   )

Comment: TRY THESE RHYTHMIC PHRASES

Five minutes after.
A second hawk.
Without tragic result.
When the sky cleared.
The branch of a tree.
The field of observation.
Defending her young.

Give a word for action beginning with 'p'.
The top of rising ground beginning with (invisible) 'h'.
The name of a bird beginning with 'h'.
The name of a bird beginning with 'm'.

Write the account at dictation.
(Original—mostly observation—contributed and arranged as lip-reading practice.)

| **LESSON 8** | *Making Your Own Subject* |

Clue Subject: MY HOLIDAY AT HITCHIN IN HERT-FORDSHIRE

Method of Study—Invisible initial letters will be *italicised*. Do not concentrate on them as such, but on the whole flow of your sentence and subject. I *italicise* them just to remind you that they do exist, and are one of the objects of our study, *in their context*.

Clue Sentence: I HAVE JUST RETURNED FROM MY HOLIDAY

1. I visited a friend in *h*er charming *c*ottage and *g*arden.

2. The *c*ottage, of *c*ourse, was in the *g*arden, and the *g*arden is in a forty-acre meadow.

3. My bedroom is the *g*arden room. Outside my bedroom are two old apple trees. These apple trees are dead, but their branches make a playground for the birds—baby birds, and parent birds.

4. The birds are very busy first thing in the morning. They *h*ave their bath and *c*lean their

feathers. Every feather is carefully cleaned above and below. They clean their beaks on a twig. The feathers float into my bedroom.

5. In front of my bedroom are flower gardens. I say flower-gardens because they truly describe the garden. The flower-beds are within three lawns of fine grass. Each little flower-garden is separated by a pergola of rambling roses; a trellis of climbing clematis, or an arbour of hazel bushes.

6. Behind the garden-room is a plantation of plum and pear trees. It is flecked with sunshine and shadow. It gives shelter from the heat all day long. Beyond the fence is a forty-acre meadow, and a few fat calves of a neighbouring farmer—and not a house to be seen.

7. This holiday I was fortunate. I saw what I have never seen before. I would call it "The Festival of the Family Flight of Birds." Great flocks of birds flew into the apple trees about dawn. I think they must have been migrants, resting. After much activity in the trees, they flew away.

8. These are some of the birds we have recognised in the garden:—
Finches and fly-catchers,
Robins and wrens,
Warblers and wag-tails,
Green woodpeckers and spotted woodpeckers.

The deaf and dumb demonstrate their Finger Alphabet to visitors at their Christmas party. The use of the alphabetical signs familiarly used by the dumb are occasionally found worthwhile for the hard of hearing. Ask when in doubt about words initiated by letters that look alike.

'ANCIENT AND MODERN'

Hand-made (white funnel and rubber tubing); "telescopic trumpet" and "rotating trumpet"—probably "antiques"—and other clumsy forms of trumpet type give place to the modern forms of amplification, including the government hearing aid (1948) and the later 'transistors'. Complementary to them all and in line with the 'Synthetic' method of Lip-reading are the radio and the television. All these aural and visual aids are invaluable for concentration on the mouth.

Unity Hall, Torquay, together with three smaller rooms was made available as an experimental centre for lip-reading and speech work and other developments by the kindness and generosity of the Church Council.

This property, recently purchased as a Town Centre for Handicapped Persons, shows further promise of developments as a possible over-all pattern in the same one town towards the relief of the limitations of handicapped people, and the ideal of living abundantly.

9. This *holiday haunt* is in a 'green belt'.
Song-thrush and missel-thrush
Blackbirds in every bush.
*H*edge-sparrows and *h*ouse sparrows,
*G*reen finches and *g*oldfinches,
Blue tits and *g*reat tits,
*C*oal tits, long-tailed tits.
Pigeons and doves,
Rooks and crows,
Yellow *h*ammer and linnet,
Whitethroat and lesser whitethroat,
Swifts and swallows,
Robin, wren and willow-wren,
*C*uckoo and *k*estrel,
Starling,
Barn owl and little barn owl.

10. My friend *h*as seen all these birds in *h*er *g*arden this year. They are robbing the rust-red berries from the rowan tree.

(This, too, is an original contribution—valuable self-expression on hobby lines, that of bird-watching.)

Mirror Work

Study the following words in your mirror. Notice that each begins with a letter invisible to the lip-reader. The initial letter is therefore no longer an initial clue to the word. The initial vowel or 'shape' letters, together with the rhythm, are then the strongest clues for the word-study.

holiday	cottage	garden
hazel-nut	climbing clematis	ground
heat	calves	grass
house	coal-tit	goldfinch
hedge	cuckoo	
	kestrel	
	crows	

Notice the effect of 'r' following 'g' or 'c' in the words 'ground' and 'grass' and 'crows'.

Study Notes (Paragraph by paragraph.)

1. After reading the whole, study these selections for invisible letter consciousness through vowel shape, leading to word shape and rhythm in their context.

h. My *h*oliday at Hitchin in *H*ertfordshire

c. The *c*ottage of *c*ourse

g. The *g*arden 'the *g*reen belt'

2. Spot the movement of the consonants *b* and *p* (looking alike).

 Bedroom, baby birds, parent birds, branches.

3. Continue using these phrases. (*b* and add *f*, teeth to lips.)

b. Birds are busy, their bath, their beaks, above and below.

f. First thing, every feather, feathers float.

4. Continue to consider f, and invisible g, h.

f. In front, flower-*g*ardens, fine *g*rass.

h. *H*azel-nut.

5. Revision of f and p and b.

b.   behind,   beyond.

p.   plantation of plum and pear, plum and pear (couplet).

f.   forms the foreground, flecked with sunshine, the fence, a few fat calves, neighbouring farmer.

6. Continue to recognise f in:
   festival of the family flight of birds.
   flew away.
   flock of birds flew.

LESSON 9 | *Try Writing your own Short Story*

THE CHRISTMAS TOUCH

A FEW minutes to midnight, and Santa Claus trudged along, on foot now, looking for the right home for the gifts of his special liking. He knew he would find it, for he had never failed to empty his sacks. And he found it almost on the brow of the hill. It was much like the other houses, but it was, nevertheless, unlike them.

Santa Claus opened the gate. A few flowers of the year that was passing hung their heads, and many flowers of the coming year nestled in the rich, red soil, awaiting their turn to glorify the earth.

He reached the door and waited—a door shining bright in the moonlight. Where the knocker should have been, a spray of holly hung, delicately beautiful, its balanced growth tied with ribbons of pristine white and red. Where the bell-push should have been, a little hole—the only thing he could find that was not just ready for Christmas. And between the two, a shining, shining door-handle, which responded readily to his touch. Before entering, he looked from one window to another. In one, a bowl of holly, carefully selected and lovingly placed. In the other, crimson cyclamen bowed their heads with the adoring world.

Santa Claus entered the little bungalow and looked, first at one and then at the other of the sleepers. Then he went back to the hall and left his gifts there in the space exactly proportioned for them. As he turned to shut the gate he paused and looked at the decorated door, shining in the moonlight. He thought of the delicate lady within, and of her son, who would be the first to see the gifts—a table, the work of a perfect craftsman; and mirrored in its polished surface, the books, bound in leather soft as satin, the letters illuminated by a master hand. 'Self-sacrifice, peace and love in action' they spelled, and on the top, a crown of purest gold.

Somewhere he heard a hand-bell. 'Ding-dong, Ding-dong, Ding-dong,' and, according to custom, the old town-crier calling; "At the Nativity of Our Lord, the angels sang with one accord . . . Quarter past twelve on a bright, starlight morning. Ding-dong."

'The gifts of his special liking'—for the homes of his special liking, of course. "Christ in a human life" he whispered, as he shut the gate. And he breathed the name 'Christian'.

Original.

PREPARATION AND PRACTICE

Aim

To notice the words containing long vowels or diphthongs (the union of two vowels pronounced as one sound).

Method

Whether listening or reading, look out for words that are repeated, and recognise them as old friends. Look out for clue words through the whole story.

Diphthongs (see Table in Appendix 1)

ay as in	*ie* as in	*oy* as in	*ou* as in	*oh* as in
failed	night	soil	brow	bowl
gate	right		now	growth
spray	find		found	only
placed	light		houses	hole
space	white		flowers	
table	life		bound	
name	Christ			
waited	liking			
awaiting	unlike			
	shining bright			
	moonlight			
	sacrifice			

Look out for repetitions

e.g.

A few flowers of the year that was passing.

Many flowers of the coming year.

He reached the door.

A door shining bright in the moonlight.

A shining, shining door-handle.

The right home for the gifts of his special liking.

The gifts of his special liking, for the homes of his special liking, of course.

Notice in passing: association of ideas, in sequence (lesson 5) around the word 'gifts', e.g.

The gifts: the table, the work of a perfect crafts-man; the books, bound in leather, soft as satin, the letters illuminated by a master-hand . . . and on the top, a crown of purest gold.

Treat this sentence as 'extensions':—

Mirrored in its polished surface, the books, bound in leather, soft as satin, the letters illuminated by a master-hand.

Thus:

Mirrored in its polished surface, the books.

Mirrored in its polished surface, the books, bound in leather.

Mirrored in its polished surface, the books, bound in leather, soft as satin.

Mirrored in its polished surface, the books, bound in leather, soft as satin, the letters illuminated by a master-hand.

LESSON 10 | *From an Anthology of Poetry*

An Old World Creed

I believe
In all things beautiful—
The beauty of simple things.

I believe in Music where
Melody is quickly found and
In poems that sound like song.

I believe in books that hold no ugly thought,
In pictures that rest the eye and soothe the
    senses,
And in plays that keep the heart young.

Little things delight me:
A sunbeam on a blade of grass:
A dewdrop in the heart of a flower;
A daisy with a rosy frill.

I believe in joy, and quick laughter;
In Sentiment, in Love, in Reverence.

I believe in all things beautiful.
    I BELIEVE IN GOD.

                                M. Aumonier.

Study

How words beginning with 'explosive' letters are
made on the lips.

b	p	m
believe	poems	music
beauty	pictures	
beautiful	plays	
books		
blade		

Each initial letter is a movement, each looking the same, but not to be mistaken in the words.

Phrases

I believe. The beauty of simple things. I believe in books. I believe in pictures. I believe in plays. A blade of grass.

Invisible Letters

hold . . . books that *h*old no ugly thought.

heart . . . plays that *k*eep the *h*eart young.

h . . . the *h*eart of a flower.

grass . . . a blade of *g*rass.

More Words with Initial Letters made on the lips (teeth to lip).

f

found . . . Melody is found.

flower . . .In the heart of a flower

frill . . . A daisy with a rosy frill.

Now the whole poem, without hearing.

| LESSON 11 | *Extracts from Books* |

THE DAY IS OURS
by Hilda Lewis* (the Mandy Story)

1. Listen, or read into your mirror:

Clue Subject: MANDY IS PUZZLED AT REACTIONS TO SPEECH.

'What happens when the bird, the cat, father, mother, etc. open their mouths?'

2. Notice the word shapes as you listen or read them into your mirror.

The cat opened its mouth and a saucer of milk was put down.

Father moved his mouth and mother brought him the paper, or his pipe, or shut the window.

Val moved her mouth, and mother did up a button, or gave her a book, a pen, or a pencil.

Then her mind leaped. She had no words. She knew the desolation of one who was shut out.

* Published by Jarrolds.

3. Notice the easiest clue letters, made on the lips, outside the teeth.

Initial movement letters: p, b, m looking alike.

b	p	m
bird	paper	mouth
button	pipe	milk
book	pen	mother
brought	pencil	mind

4. Lip-read the clue sentences in paragraph 2.

Exercise

Speak into your mirror the simple sentences in the previous exercises.

Now a passage from the book which the film 'Mandy' was made. (She was Tamsy in the book.)

"All the time—at the back of her mind—a question.

"What happened when the bird, Mother, Father, Val and David opened their mouths and shut them again? . . . It was something she *had* to know . . . Now she thought about it, she knew that everybody in the house opened and shut them again. And then something always happened. Someone did something, went to get something, or moved a mouth in return— always something . . . and always it was the right thing.

"She had always known that, of course. But she hadn't taken particular notice. Now she began to watch intently.

"Then suddenly, her mind leaped."

Shape and movement, shape and movement. Like Mandy, 'you have always known that, of course.' But you have the additional help of knowing shape and movement in relation to sound. In the back of your mind, subconsciously, you have always known it. Ability to bring it to your conscious mind will enable *you* to work on the Synthetic Method, with its 'Progress through Interest', and *me* not to fuss you with phonetic charts, though I append one for those who may wish to refer to it. We really need not talk about 'diphthongs', short and long vowels, etc. We know that BOY is made up of the shape of 'oy' with the movement of 'b' before it. Such words with two elements in them will be found as you work through your *Guide Work Book* 1.

It is good practice now to make up conversations, descriptions, questions and answers for yourself, speaking them into your mirror. It doesn't matter that you know what you are saying. Your mind is beginning to recognise why it is what it is, and your eye to check up, your subconscious mind to store.

LESSON 12

Harder Selections

from *Wind, Sand and Stars**
by Antoine de Saint-Exupéry

FROM now onwards my selections are rather more difficult. But they will, I hope, show you how you need not be alone in your deafness, how you can make thoughts your companions.

Clue Subjects

1. 'OUR THINKING ALTERS WHAT WE GENERALLY SEE.'
2. 'THE WORLD UNFOLDS BEFORE OUR ADVENTUROUS THINKING.'

Read through quickly:

A. 1. Have you come across a book called *Wind, Sand and Stars*?
   2. It is written by a French airman.
   3. He flew air mails across the desert—the Sahara desert.

* Published by Wm. Heinemann.

4. He took his mails from South West France to West Africa.

5. He crashed in the desert.

B. 6. He had the most amazing adventures.

7. He suffered the most ghastly agony of thirst and fatigue.

C. 8. At the end of it all he looked back to:—
'Where we set out to fly our first mails.'
'Where we prepared ourselves to be transformed into men . . .'
'We, who had the luck to be called . . . To be called to be men—through suffering.'

D. 9. 'To come to manhood, it is not necessary to get oneself killed, or to fly mail planes out of respect for the dignity of life. The man who can see the miraculous in a poem, who can take pure joy from music; who opens his windows to the wind off the sea—he, too, learns a language of men.

'But too many men are left unawakened.'

PREPARATION

Association of Ideas

A. CLUES: 1. A French Airman . . . Air Mails . . .
(repetition: Air)

2. Flying . . . across desert . . . the Sahara
   Desert, *from* S. W. France . . . *to*
   French Africa.

Build up A. (above) so far.

B. CLUE: Amazing Adventures
   Suffered . . . ghastly agonies . . . thirst and
   fatigue.

Build up B.

C. CLUES: 1. At the end, two thoughts.
   (*a*) 'Our thinking alters what we generally
        see.' What suffering did for us.
   (*b*) 'The world unfolds before our adven-
        turous thinking.' ('The man who
        can see the miraculous . . .')

Build up C.

D. Switch off.

DICTATION

I remember where . . .

I remember where we set out to fly our first mail,
when we prepared ourselves to be transformed into
men—we, who had had the luck to be called . . .
(to be called to be men—through suffering.)

To come to man's estate it is not necessary to get
oneself killed or to fly mail planes out of respect for
the dignity of life. The man who can see the
miraculous in a poem, who can take pure joy from

music, who can open his windows to the refreshing wind off the sea—he too, learns a language of men.

But too many men are left unawakened.

ANALYSIS

Do you recognise your shapes and movements?

Picture of Clue Words

i	a	ar(ah)
wind	sand	stars
written	Africa	Sahara
dignity	crashed	France
	amazing	ghastly agony
	adventures	
	agony	
	fatigue	

Clue Subject: THE COMMANDANT'S GARDEN

Listen or read—Our airman shows how we care for the little things that we cherish in the desert.

"One evening we dined at the fort and the commandant showed off his 'garden' to us. Someone had sent him, from France, three thousand miles away, a few boxes of real soil, and out of the soil grew three green leaves which we caressed as if they had been jewels. The commandant would say of them: 'This is my park'. And when there arose one of those sand-storms that shrivelled everything up, he would move the 'park' down into the cellars."

B

Points You Might Study

Did the invisible letters strike you as you read through these passages?

care, commandant, garden, grew, green, caressed, came, calling, great, guessing, coming, catching, gone.

Remembering that you cannot see the initial letter, try to recognise the word by the shape of the whole in the context in which it is found, as well as by the rhythm of the word, e.g.

The *commandant* showed off his *garden*. Out of the soil *grew* three *green* leaves. I *guessed* what I was expecting.

Look out for any suggestions of associated ideas, e.g. Soil . . . grew . . . leaves. These things will be flashing through your mind, and checking up for you by this time.

Make a list and run through all the words in which 's', double 's', 'z' or 'c' sounding like 's' occur. Speak them into your mirror and let it register on your mind what they look like.

How Sensitive our Airman Becomes

"I was to take my radio officer on this flight. I said: 'Everything all right?' For the moment everything was all right. But I heard something sizzling. It was a dragonfly knocking against my lamp. And again I felt a dull ache which might as easily have been joy as fear, but came up from the depths of me . . . Someone was calling me from a great distance. Was it instinct?

"I had received a warning. I guessed what I was expecting. Was I right? Neither the sky nor the sand had made the least sign to me: but two dragon-flies and a moth had spoken.

"If I was right the thing would not be long coming. What were they after here, those dragonflies, hundreds of miles from their oasis island? . . . These insects declared to me that a sandstorm was on the way . . . In the seconds that followed, the Sahara was catching its breath, and would send forth a second sigh . . . Before ten minutes had gone by, the sand would fill the air . . . but it was not that that excited me. What filled me with joy . . . was that I was to read the anger of the desert in the beating wings of a dragonfly."

THOUGHTS AS COMPANIONS

Clue Subject: OUR AIRMAN TAKES SOME MOORS TO FRANCE

Read or listen: They saw the Eiffel Tower, the steamships, the locomotives and a circus.

"These Moors took very little trouble to show the indifference they felt for the Eiffel Tower, the steamships, the locomotives or the French women who can stand jumping from one galloping horse to another. (What they thought admirable was not the locomotives, but a tree.)

(And his 'thoughts as companions'.)

"When you think of it, a tree does possess a perfection that a locomotive does not, cannot know. And then I remembered the Moors who had wept at the sight of the trees . . . Here were men who had never seen a tree, a river, a rose; who only knew through the Koran of the existence of gardens where streams run, which is their name for paradise . . .

"You know. . . the God of the French . . . He is more generous to the French than the God of the Moors is to the Moors."

Wind, Sand and Stars—this airman's reminiscences —will give you many lovely passages to read into your mirror, if you are a lone lip-reader, or keen to practise alone.

NOTICE in these passages the projection followed by relaxed lips to form 'r' as in:—remember, river, run, trees, stream, paradise.

Lip-read his thoughts as companions from:

"When you think of it a tree does possess a perfection . . ."

Use it as a piece of 'translation':

1. Read it, conscious of the shapes on the printed page.

2. 'Translate' it, conscious of the spoken shapes.

Clue Subject: 'IN THE COURSE OF A LONG RAILWAY JOURNEY.'

"In the course of a long railway journey I went through the train in all its length. The sleeping cars were empty . . . but the third-class carriages were crowded with hundreds of Polish workmen sent home from France. A whole nation returning to its native poverty seemed to sprawl there in a sea of bad dreams . . . Men, women and children were stirring in their sleep . . . they had not found the hospitality of sweet slumber . . .

"These people had been knocked about from one end of Europe to another . . . they had been torn from their little homes in the north of France, from their tiny garden plots, their three pots of geraniums that always stood in the windows of Polish miners' families.

"Out of all that they had caressed or loved in France, out of everything they had succeeded in taming in their four or five years in my country—the cat, the dog, the geranium—they had been able to bring away with them only a few kitchen utensils, two or three blankets, a curtain or two.

'I sat down face to face with one couple. Between the man and the woman, a child had fallen asleep.'

Clue Subject: HIS THOUGHTS AS COMPANIONS

"What an adorable face! . . This is a musician's face. This is the child Mozart. This is a life full of beautiful promise . . . protected, sheltered, cultivated, what could not this child become?

"When a new rose is born in a garden, all the gardeners rejoice. They tend it, foster it. But there is no gardener for men. This little Mozart will be shaped like the rest of the common stamping machine. This little Mozart will love shoddy music. This little Mozart is condemned.

"I went back to my sleeping car. I said to myself: 'I do not believe in pity . . . what torments me is not this poverty to which, after all, a man can accustom himself as easily as to sloth. Generations of Orientals live in filth, and love it. What torments me . . . is the sight, a little bit of all these men, of Mozart murdered.

"'Only the spirit, if it breathe upon the clay, can create Man.'"

Read again 'His Thoughts as Companions', so as thoroughly to absorb the thought, the more unusual words and the less obvious associations.

Then try lip-reading a little of it, conscious of 'translating' print shapes into speech shapes.

Notice the 'flicking' movement of the tongue behind the teeth in sounding 'l' as the initial or clue letter in:

long, length, little, loved, life.

Notice the same movement at the ends of the words:

all, sprawl, utensil, couple, full, beautiful, will, oriental, unusual.

Make your own list of words from this passage which have the 'l' movement in the middle of the word. Speak them into your mirror.

Refer to your chart and notice to which group they belong, and why.

Notice the similarity of movement when you sound the letter 'n' in the words: nation, native, notion.

Speak into your mirror also words containing 'n' in the middle, noticing the movement there.

Now look for, and use in the same way words ending with 'n'.

| **LESSON 13** | *Harder Selections* |

Adapted from *The Spring of Joy** by Mary Webb

READ the following into your mirror.

A. *Clue Subject:* 'A BREATH OF THE COUNTRY'

The power of this life if men will open their hearts

* Published by Jonathan Cape.

to it, will heal them, will create men anew. . . . physically and spiritually. . . .

We need no new gifts . . The way is through love of beauty and reality . . . a humble mind and a receptive heart. We must go softly if we desire the butterfly's confidence; we must walk humbly if we dare to ask for an interpretation of this dream of God.

No accident of environment or circumstance can cut us off from Nature. Her spirit stirs the flowers in a town window-box, looks up from the eyes of a dog, sounds from the chirp of a grimy city sparrow. . . . One flower is as sweet as an acre of them. And it often happens—as if by a kindly law of compensation—that those who have only one violet find the way through its narrow purple gate into the land of God, while many who walk over dewy carpets of them do not as much as know there is a land or a way.

. . . We think there is some deep meaning in it all, if we could only find it. . . . It is this sense of mystery . . . that gives glory to the countryside, tenderness to the atmosphere. . . . For in each of us is implanted a threefold capacity for loving his fellow and nature and the Creator of them both.

B. *Clue Subject:* 'NECESSITIES OF OUR NATURE'

Beauty and Joy and Laughter are necessities of our being, and Nature brims with them. There are some things that always bring joy. . . . The coming of Spring brings it—the first crocus pricking up, dawn a moment earlier day by day, the mist of green on the honeysuckle hedges in February . . . The flawless days of May bring it, when the white lilac is out and purple lilac is breaking from the bud, and the chestnut spires are lengthening, and the hawthorn will not be long.

Out in the fresh, green world, where the thrushes sing so madly, the sweets of the morning are waiting to be gathered . . . You fling the window wide to the dawn, and lean out into the clear purity before the light, listening to the early 'chuck, chuck' of the blackbird . . . Then the air is full of wings; the birds fly in and out of the trees, scattering showers of raindrops as they dash from leafy chestnut . . . and over all are the brooding wings of unknown presences . . .

Since the fact of seeing it is a precious thing, let us go out along the lovely ways that lead from our door into the heart of enchantment.

Ceasing for a time to question and strive, let us dare to be merely receptive—stepping lightly over the dewy meadows, brushing no blue dust from the butterfly's wings. Then, if life is suddenly simplified by the removal of all we hold most dear, we shall know the way to other things, not less precious. We shall know of long, green vistas, carpeted with speedwell, ascending to a place of comfort, and the blue butterfly will lead us into peace.

E*

Revise, in your mirror, any words that you found difficult, e.g. those beginning with invisible initial letters—green vistas, gifts, grimy, gate. 'Gives glory to the countryside.' Capacity, Creator, comfort, confidence. 'Kindly law of compensation,' heart, humbly.

Find others or use these in sentences of your own.

ASSOCIATION OF IDEAS

Try to associate some of these picturesque ideas with personal reminiscences.

Idea 1.—'We must go softly if we desire the butterfly's confidence.'

Personal Association.—'As children, we used to try to catch the small blue butterfly by its folded wings, when it settled on the flowers of the field; then we would send it floating into the air, or restore it to its nectar.'

Idea 2.—'Nature's spirit sounds in the chirp of the grimy city sparrow.'

Personal Association.—'I remember an invalid, wheeled daily to the public gardens. Scores of sparrows always awaited him, to be fed. They do not come now, for he is dead!'

Idea 3.—'Only one violet.'

Personal Association.—'Every spring a friend of mine, who is an artist, paints for me the first spring flowers to unfold in her garden.'

Idea 4.—'There is some deep mystery in it all.'
Personal Association.—'We feel the love of the Creator for them.'

The walk before breakfast gives it; the dew on cobwebs; song-birds' pre-dawn twitter, dawn-song, love-song. Pink larch catkins give it; pussy willows: lambs' tails; hawk moths—deep mysteries indeed.

LESSON 14 | *Harder Selections*

Extract from *The Snow Goose** by Paul Gallico

Method.—Read the passage through, into your mirror.

Fritha found Rayader's paintings stacked in the Lighthouse.

She found among the pictures one of herself, hugging the injured bird to her.

The picture and the things she saw in it stirred her as nothing ever had before, for much of Rayader's soul had gone into it. Strangely, it was the only time

* Published by Michael Joseph, 26, Bloomsbury Street, W.C.1.

he had painted the snow goose, the lost, wild creature, storm-driven from another land . . .

Long before the snow goose had come dropping out of a crimson sky to circle the lighthouse in a last farewell . . . Fritha knew that Rayader would not return.

And so, when one sunset, she heard the high-pitched note cried from the heavens . . . it brought no hope to her heart.

She came running to the sea-wall and turned her eyes, not to the sea whence a sail might come, but to the sky to which the snow goose had soared. Then the sight, the sound, and the solitude surrounding . . . released the surging, overwhelming truth of her love, and let it well forth in tears . . .

Wild spirit called to wild spirit, and she seemed to be flying with the great bird, soaring with it in the evening sky, and hearkening to Rayader's message.

Sky and earth were trembling with it. "Fritha! Fritha! Fritha! My love. Goodbye, my love." The white pinions were beating it out upon her heart, and her heart was answering: "Philip, I love 'ee." . . .

She stretched her arms up to the sky and stood on tip-toes, reaching, and cried: "God speed! God speed, Philip."

Fritha's tears were stilled. She stood watching silently long after the bird had vanished. Then she went into the lighthouse and secured the picture that

Rayader had painted of her. Hugging it to her breast she wound her way homeward along the seawall.

STUDY, ACCOMPANYING THE PASSAGE

Aim.—To study to overcome the difficult initial letters, either invisible or made behind the teeth, or with little movement e.g. 'a' with closed teeth.

Invisible initial letters	Formed behind the teeth	Extended mouth and closed teeth
herself	nothing	stirred
hugging	lost	soul
had	driven	strangely
gone	land	sea
creature	long	sail
come	lighthouse	sky
crimson	last	snow
heard	turned	soared
high-pitched	truth	sight
cried	love	sound
heavens	let	solitude
hope	tears	surrounding
heart	tremble	surging
called	tip-toes	stretched
great		stood
hearkening		silently
goodbye		secured
God-speed		
homeward		

Try a few phrases

Among the pictures one of herself.

The snow goose had come to circle the lighthouse in a last farewell.

One sunset she heard the high-pitched note cried from the heavens.

She stretched her arms to the sky and stood on tip-toes.

Fritha's tears were stilled.

Wild spirit called to wild spirit.

"God-speed! God-speed! Philip!"

She wound her way homeward along the sea-wall.

Can you guess why I have chosen these sentences? Say them into your mirror, then guess after you have noticed anything special about initial movements.

LESSON 15	*Schoolboy Howlers and Comic Stories*

TRY TO LET A JOKE COME TO YOU READILY:
STUDY MATERIAL

CAN you correct these schoolboy mistakes?
Q. Why did the Israelites make a golden calf?

A. The Israelites made a golden calf because they hadn't enough gold to make a golden cow.

Q. What is the masculine of lady-bird?

A. The masculine of lady-bird sounds as if it should be gentleman-bird, but this looks funny.

Q. What is the plural of forget-me-not?

A. Forget-us-not.

Q. What is the meaning of the word 'blizzard'?

A. The inside of a fowl is called a blizzard.

Q. What is a magnet?

A. A magnet is a thing you find in bad apples.

Q. What do you know of Columbus?

A. Columbus discovered America, and was the first man.

Q. What is the Royal Mint?

A. The Royal Mint is what the King puts on his roast lamb.

Q. What is a cataract?

A. A cataract is a cat that catches rats.

A city child gave the following answer to the question: 'Give the signs that spring is here?'

A. We knew that spring is here because the cuckoo is heard in the fields, and Wall's ice cream man is on the roads.

If a gentleman is out with his wife or sweetheart, he should walk on the curve.

When making a cake, if you put the slices of candied peel on the top of the cake when it is half cooked instead of when making it, it will not fall in the middle of the cake as often happens with amateur cooks.

Could you improve upon these?

Q. What is the difference between sheep and mutton?
A. A sheep is mutton covered with wool.
 (Do you agree?)
Q. Upon what do moths feed?
A. Moths do not eat much, because they feed on holes.
Q. What is the opposite of evergreen?
A. The opposite of evergreen is nevergreen.

Uncle knew that John was keen on moths and butterflies. When he visited him at school, he gave him half a crown to spend on anything he liked.

On his next visit, he asked John: "Well John! How did you spend your half crown?" He was surprised that John looked disappointed. "Well?"

"I bought a book called 'Advice to Young Mothers'."

The Inspector came into the classroom to test the children's tables. The answers came very readily . . .

$$6 \times 7 \ldots 42$$
$$9 \times 9 \ldots 81$$
$$3 \times 8 \ldots 24$$

Very good. Very good.

Now try this one. 11 x 11 . . . No Answer.

Oh come! Surely somebody knows 11 x 11 . . . No Answer.

Come. Tell me. Who does know 11 x 11?

The dull boy sitting in the far corner rises slowly, and puts up his hand. "Please Sir, Gawd knows."

A small boy in a junior class was making a meal of some chewing-gum.

"Peter," commanded the teacher, "come out and throw that gum into the waste-paper basket."

Peter emerged from his seat, but on reaching the waste-paper basket stood still and began to cry. When he was asked to explain, he cried: "I'll cop it, Miss, when I get home; my brother only lent me the gum for the afternoon."

Coming home from school along a country lane a little boy and girl met a herd of cows. The little girl was very frightened.

"O come on," said the boy bravely. "Cows never hurt you."

The little girl hesitated, looking anxiously at the oncoming cow.

"Yes," she replied, "but when a cow looks like that, it's a bull."

RIDDLE

What is the difference between a Riddle and an Elephant sitting on a bun?

One is a Conundrum; the other is a Bun under 'im.

A small boy entered the church alone, and was shown up to the front by the verger. He was given no books, and he soon became bored.

A kindly old soul noticed him, and put him into the empty seat in front of her, and she found his places for him, but he was still bored. So when people kneeled down to pray, he played trains with his books along the book-rail.

"Oh, oh, oh! . . ." he said aloud.

An old man in front of him turned round, and held up his finger, saying: "Sh, sh, sh! . . ."

The small boy looked up at him, and said: "Do you like playing trains too?"

Margaret, aged four, and David, aged seven, went out to tea with their Grandmother.

After tea they went to the garden to see the fowls, but Margaret preferred the flowers.

David was told that all the fowls had names. "That one is called Henrietta," his hostess said.

David was amused. "Look, Margaret, all these fowls have names." And forgetting which one, he said: "That one is called Henrietta."

"Don't be silly, David," Margaret replied. "That one's a cock, so it must be called Cockrietta."

An Exercise in Charting your Studies

DAVID'S AND MARGARET'S VISIT TO AN OLD
FRIEND

1	2	3	4	5
	Less		*Less*	
Easy	*easy*	*Difficult*	*Difficult*	*Others*
m, r	f	g, h, c	n, t, d, l, k	s, ch
				(contrast)
Margaret	finally	guests	David	silly
Margaret	family	grandmother	David	children
Margaret	four	hostess	David	
Margaret	friend	garden	like	
must	fowls	go	names	
Margaret	fowls	Henrietta	lady	
	fowls	called	look	
		come	don't	
		have	David	
		called	can't	
		Henrietta	called	
			cook	
			Cockrietta	

Making this kind of chart will help you to realise
how often certain letters appear in a study. So,
with conscious practice, your mind will automatically
find them, or fill in the invisible initials, as your
fingers do in typing. (For a full analytical chart of
the movement letters or consonants, see Appendix 1, 3).

EPILOGUE

I HAVE enjoyed writing these notes, for as I have been writing them I have felt a kind of mystical contact with those for whom I have been writing. Lip-reading has given me also widening contacts with next to no embarrassment as I use my hearing aid and lip-reading together—and it has broken down my diffidence in meeting and talking to other people. I give it as my personal experience that this rather difficult handicap is not all loss, by any means. I have found thoughts most companionable, and the habit of contemplation which many years of deafness has formed for me has proved an immense and purposeful interest, as well as a great relaxation, so sadly needed by hard-of-hearing people, for they are more on the strain, I think, than the totally deaf, and seldom know it until the pain of strain sets in.

Another valuable gain for me has been concentration. The lack of it once hampered me in many ways, especially in learning and in performing musical and dramatic arts.

Albert Schweitzer said that the present world needs nothing so much as the formation of the habit of deep thinking. How much this suggestion has helped me to find thoughts companionable; to be glad that enforced early retirement gave me time for them. I began to make a hobby of them with my already well-thumbed Bible, and with a pencil in hand I carefully annotated, as one would with other studies, the passages that appealed to me, or which aroused provocative thought, or new enlightenment—this latter, particularly, as I read the Knox edition of the New Testament in modern English. Other thought-provoking books followed, and I began to find myself making new contacts with like-minded people, who gave me opportunities to express as well as to be impressed, and I found myself losing my fear that interests would slip away.

Church-going became what I could give, instead of what I could get out of it, in thoughts and prayers —the orthodox ones, at my own pace; or my own thoughts in prayer form. The words of hymns became more meaningful when I found myself unable to join in the tunes adequately. (My lip-reading now enables me to sing them again, watching the choir to keep my pace correct, and I no longer sing verse four, which I did not hear the priest ask us to omit!) I am able again to take up public speaking and discussion, for my hearing aid and my imperfect lip-reading together give me back much of my 'hearing', and I feel I can now go about, 'bearing with me the infection of a good courage to press on towards the mark'.

So let us go on, unfolding our lives; making the

negative positive. Let us cease to strive, remembering that Christ, the great Healer, did not say: 'Take up thy bed and run!', but: 'Take up thy bed and walk', meaning perhaps: 'God helps those who help themselves at whatever pace they can'. In so doing we shall recollect also how He expressed Himself in the pattern of His life, as Kipling did also in the poetry of his words:

> "It isn't the fact that you're hurt that counts,
> But only: 'How did you take it'."

APPENDIX 1

CHARTS OF SHAPE AND MOVEMENT IN RELATION TO SOUND

Aim—To become shape and movement conscious in watching the lips.

Remember—Letters 'say' something in relation to their sound. And do voice these charts as you study them. It makes a lot of difference.

1. Sound the long vowels:

ar	as in	far
ee	as in	fee
aw	as in	paw
oo	as in	pool

2. Sound the short vowels:

a	as in	apple
e	as in	egg or elephant
i	as in	ink
o	as in	orange
u	as in	up or umbrella

(You are sounding them, aren't you? Not naming them?)

3. Movement Letters (Consonants)

    (*a*) Easy, because movement is well pronounced, outside the teeth, on the lips.

letter	formed by	as in
p b m	lips meeting and parting (explosives)	pot bobbin moth
f v	upper teeth to lower lip	father view
sh ch j soft g w	projected lips, puckered at corners	shell church jug ginger Woolworth

3. (*b*) Less easy, because less pronounced, with less movement of lips.

letter	formed by	as in
r y	lips slightly puckered at corners	rabbit yellow
s soft c z	extended lips and closed teeth, the sound hissed through the teeth	sister celandine zebra

3. (*c*) Difficult, because almost invisible—made in the throat.

letter	*formed by*	*as in*
h		happy
g	a breath through the mouth	gap
c	formed in the throat	cap
k		kipper

(*d*) Less difficult, but still difficult, because made with the tongue, behind the teeth.

letter	*formed by*	*as in*
n		naughty
t	tongue pressed to palate behind	temper
d	teeth	dip
l		lily

4. Diphthongs (combination of two vowels into one sound)

In practice, you may well think of these as being the same as long vowels, though when analysed they prove to consist of two short ones united.

$$ay \quad \text{as in} \quad day \quad (e+i)$$
$$ie \quad \text{as in} \quad die \quad (a+i)$$
$$oh \quad \text{as in} \quad grow \quad (o+u)$$
$$ou \quad \text{as in} \quad house \quad (a+u)$$
$$oy \quad \text{as in} \quad boy \quad (o+i)$$

APPENDIX 2

Leaflet issued by the British Association of the Hard of Hearing (Incorporating organisations for Lip-Reading and the Deafened)

THE IMPORTANCE OF LIP-READING

As a rule, doctors recommend that people who use hearing aids should also practise the art of lip-reading. Many people ask why this is necessary.

If they stop to think about it, they must realise that a hearing aid is an electrical device which *aids* hearing but cannot fully restore it. Tests have proved that those who use an aid still cannot understand 100 per cent of the conversation which is going on around them, but these tests also show that the margin of loss below 100 per cent is very materially reduced if the hearing aid is combined with lip-reading. How much is seen and how much is heard does not matter—IT IS THE TWO COMBINED that brings better understanding.

As the hearing aid is a mechanical device it can break down without warning. Remember, too, that hearing may quite likely deteriorate as one grows older. Prudent people will not wait for this to happen but will take steps at once to learn lip-reading.

No ONE is ever too old to learn, but naturally, the younger one is the easier it is.

WHY NOT, therefore, take up the study of lip-reading?

It is not a dull, dry subject; on the contrary it can be a fascinating game if you give your mind to it. Your local Club for the Hard of Hearing or Education Authority will tell you what to do. *The cost is very small and the gain is very great.*

APPENDIX 3

For Further Help: *Some Notes and Advice*

Do not attempt to take lessons from any but trained teachers. The National Institute for the Deaf and the British Association for the Hard of Hearing insist on the basic qualification of a teaching diploma prior to specialised training in teaching lip-reading.

You may want to get in touch with a local association to give you help and information. Your most reliable source for these is invariably your Local Authority Welfare Department or Education Department. They will advise you about local associations as well as helping you in other ways.

If you want to know what is being done and can be done for the deaf and hard of hearing, you should read the Ministry of Health Memorandum on Deafness, June, 1957 (on "The prevention and alleviation of deafness") and Government Circular 32/51 ("The Hard of Hearing Person's Charter").

HEARING AIDS

Any Doctor can arrange for a patient to be tested for, and fitted with, a Hearing Aid. Full and simple instructions will be given concerning its use when it is supplied to the patient or, in the case of a young child, to the parent. Remember that even a small sound indistinguishable on its own can be made intelligible by the addition of lip-reading. The conjunction of the two will mean that as time passes and if old age robs the patient of the last remnants of natural hearing, a much more efficient understanding of lip-reading will remain.

How to Use a Hearing Aid

1. Wear it as much as possible.

2. Do not be self-conscious about it—it is no different from wearing glasses.

3. Keep the microphone clear of clothing so that it can receive sounds without hindrance.

4. Keep the earpiece clean and free from wax.

5. Make sure it is switched ON—and off when not in use.

6. Change batteries regularly. They are usually provided with a space on the cover for a number—if each battery is numbered and changed consecutively each day, they will last longer and give more efficient service.

7. Use the tone device just as you tune a wireless set to cut out unwanted sounds.

8. On the telephone—(i) Turn the telephone receiver upside-down with the mouth-piece at the corner of your mouth; your amplifier as close to the telephone earpiece as may be without touching; speak as usual.

If in trouble, don't hesitate to say you are hard of hearing and ask for speech a little slower. This will probably make it clear enough without further help from increased volume, which may make awkward vibrations.

(ii) If you find any difficulty with the above method you should ask for an amplifier to be fitted to your telephone. A simple device, a boon and a blessing, it is used without your hearing aid, and enables prolonged conversation without embarrassment.

How to Wear the Batteries

This will depend largely on the patient's ingenuity. It is probably easier for men than for women, but the following suggestions may prove helpful.

For Women—Purchase at any draper's or store a man's trouser pocket. Support it by stitching tape around the edges, and add a length of the tape, enough to form a fairly large loop. The loop plus pocket may then be worn as a 'bandolier', with the batteries placed safely in the pocket. They should hang from the side opposite the amplifier (see the

lower photograph opposite page 97). If they are worn thus you will notice neither their weight nor their movement.

For Men—A pocket just large enough to take the batteries fixed to the inside of the waistband of men's trousers, above and slightly to the right of where the hip pocket is usually placed, will position them in the small of the back where they will not cause inconvenience when sitting. Tailors will usually fit such a pocket without extra charge when making a suit.

The Ministry of Health usually provide a leather case on a long strap handle with a deaf aid so that the batteries can be slung from the shoulder if preferred.